Cadbury's
SEVENTH BOOK OF
CHILDREN'S
POETRY

Beaver Books

A Beaver Book
Published by Arrow Books Limited
62-5 Chandos Place, London WC2N 4NW
An imprint of Century Hutchinson Ltd

London Melbourne Sydney Auckland
Johannesburg and agencies throughout the world

First published 1989
© Cadbury Ltd 1989

Set in Garamond by
JH Graphics Limited, Reading

Made and printed in Great Britain
by Cox & Wyman Ltd
Reading

ISBN 0 09 970600 8

Contents

Publisher's note

The poems in this book were chosen by a panel of judges which included poets, teachers and educationalists, from nearly 40,000 entries for the Poetry Section of Cadbury's 1989/90 National Exhibition of Children's Art. This year is the seventh in which there has been a poetry section and the final judges – Jennifer Curry, Chairperson of the Advisory Panel, anthologist and author; Peter Porter, poet and literary journalist; Gareth Owen, poet, novelist and playwright; and Michael Rosen, children's author, poet and anthologist – were delighted at the great variety of material. They chose as outstanding the work of Louise Bagshawe and Katie-Louise Thomas, whose poems appear on pages 116 and 178, and 62 and 67 respectively. Louise and Katie-Louise are the Italian Tour Award winners for 1989.

Louise Bagshawe comes from Wadhurst in East Sussex and is seventeen years old. She has a place to read English Literature at Christ Church College, Oxford and will start there in October 1989. Her many interests and hobbies include politics and public speaking, along with fantasy gaming and Heavy Metal.

Sixteen-year-old Katie-Louise Thomas lives in Chelsfield in Kent. She is currently studying for 'A' levels and hopes to go on to read English at university. As well as writing poetry, she runs a small Writers' Circle at her school and regularly contributes articles to her local newspaper. She plays the piano and flute, and is a keen theatre-goer – and fencer.

The Arthur Lines Poetry Award was given to Claire Davis whose poems appear on pages 65 and 120. She has also had one of these poems highly commended (page 120) by the judges, along with a further 23 children whose poems appear on pages 14, 19, 21, 26, 31, 44, 56, 57, 68, 73, 77, 82, 85, 113, 117, 128, 135, 136, 146, 150, 153, 154 and 172.

The poems have been placed into chapters to give the reader the opportunity to compare the ideas of children from as young as six to mature seventeen year olds on just about every conceivable subject. All the illustrations are taken from entries to the Art and Design section of this year's Exhibition, and they complement the poems in an unusual and pleasing way.

We are very happy to be publishing such an interesting and original book and would like to thank all the writers and artists for their superb efforts. Don't forget, there's another chance to see your poem in print in the Eighth Cadbury's Book of Poetry to be published in 1990. For details on how to enter next year's exhibition please turn to page 188.

Foreword

It must be pretty exciting to wander into a bookshop, browse amongst its shelves, find a book, open it and see your thoughts, printed in black and white, with your name as the author.

With help from Cadbury, that has happened for over 150 talented young poets from all over the country who have won a place in this year's poetry section of Cadbury's National Exhibition of Children's Art. Their poems are recorded within the pages of this book for you to enjoy. We hope that they will all continue to write, and also inspire others to enter our Exhibition.

We would like to thank our distinguished panel of judges for the tremendous job they have done. Author and anthologist Jennifer Curry, who has chaired the panel since we introduced the poetry section eight years ago, feels that this is the best book yet! For my part I am delighted and astonished by the originality of thought and ingenuity of language.

Of course, without patience and encouragement from teachers and parents this book would not exist. On behalf of the poets, we thank them for that.

I hope this book gives you as much pleasure as it gave me. As usual, royalties from sales will be donated to Save the Children Fund.

David Wellings
(Managing Director)

Cadbury's Seventh Book of Children's Poetry

AWARD WINNERS – Poetry Section
42nd National Exhibition of Children's Art 1989/90

1989 ITALIAN TOUR AWARD

Katie-Louise Thomas (16)
Chelsfield, Kent

Louise Bagshawe (17)
Woldingham School, Nr Caterham, Surrey

SCHOOL POETRY AWARDS

7 and under
St Cedd's School, Chelmsford, Essex

8–11
Cloudside County Junior School, Sandiacre, Nottingham

12–14
Debenham High School, Debenham, Stowmarket, Suffolk

15–17
Ysgol Glan-y-Mor, Pwllheli, Gwynedd

ARTHUR LINES POETRY AWARD

Claire Davis (13) Newcastle-under-Lyme School,
Newcastle-under-Lyme, Staffs

HIGHLY COMMENDED

7 and under

Richard Beaumont (7) Shottermill County First School, Haslemere, Surrey
Group Work (5/6) Nunnery Wood Primary School, Worcester
Vanessa Steele (5) White Hills Lower School, Northampton
Anna Karlin (4) London
Gemma Atkins (7) Mousehold Avenue First School, Norwich, Norfolk
Sarah Cooper (7) Havannah County Primary School, Congleton, Cheshire

8–11

Debra Maddison (8) Portobello Primary School, Chester-le-Street,
Co. Durham
Paul Heath (11) Prebendal School, Chichester, West Sussex
Julia Wearn (10) Cloudside County Junior School, Sandiacre, Nottingham

Mark Appleton (10) Northmead County Middle School, Guildford, Surrey
Thomas Grieve (8) Norwich, Norfolk
Stephen West (11) Longhaugh Primary School, Dundee
Jessica Michelson (9) London

12–14

Richard Cull (12) Bracknell, Berks
Jade Widocks (13) Bolton School Girls Division, Bolton
Anna Daniel (13) Ysgol Tryfan, Lon Powys, Bangor, Gwynedd
Adele Barrowman (14) West Calder High School, Limefield, Polbeth, West Lothian
Helen Milton (12) Darrick Wood School, Orpington, Kent
Claire Davis (13) Newcastle-under-Lyme School, Newcastle-under-Lyme, Staffs

15–17

Kathryn Simmonds (16) Digswell, Welwyn, Herts
Claire Ginn (16) Billericay School, Billericay, Essex
Magda Hewitt (16) Billericay School, Billericay, Essex
Alison Pember (16) The Grove School, St Leonards on Sea, East Sussex
Toby Brown (16) The King's School, Canterbury, Kent

42nd Exhibition Tour 1989–1990

LONDON – Natural History Museum
Cromwell Road, London SW7 5BD   Tel: 01-938 9123
Friday 27th October 1989 – Friday 1st December 1989
Open Monday to Saturday 10.00 a.m. to 6.00 p.m.
Sunday 1.00 p.m. to 6.00 p.m.

PETERBOROUGH – City Museum & Art Gallery
Priestgate, Peterborough PE1 1LF   Tel: 0733 43329
Friday 8th December 1989 – Friday 5th January 1990
Open Tuesday to Saturday 10.00 a.m. to 5.00 p.m.
Closed Sundays and Mondays.

BRISTOL – Royal West of England Academy
Queens Road, Clifton, Bristol BS8 1PX   Tel: 0272 735129
Friday 12th January 1990 – Friday 16th February 1990
Open Monday to Saturday 10.00 a.m. to 5.30 p.m.
Closed Sundays.

COVENTRY – Herbert Art Gallery & Museum
Jordan Well, Coventry CV1 5RW   Tel: 0203 832381
Friday 23rd February 1990 – Friday 30th March 1990
Open Monday to Saturday 10.00 a.m. to 5.30 p.m.
Sunday 2.00 p.m. to 5.00 p.m.

MIDDLESBROUGH – Middlesbrough Art Gallery
320 Linthorpe Rd, Middlesbrough, Cleveland TS1 4AW Tel: 0642 247445
Friday 6th April 1990 – Friday 11th May 1990
Open Tuesday to Saturday 10.00 a.m. to 6.00 p.m.
Closed Sundays and Mondays.

BOLTON – Bolton Museum & Art Gallery
Le Mans Crescent, Bolton, Lancs BL1 1SE Tel: 0204 22311 (Ext 2194)
Friday 18th May 1990 – Friday 22nd June 1990
Open Monday to Friday 9.30 a.m. to 5.30 p.m.
Saturday 10.00 a.m. to 5.00 p.m.
Closed Wednesdays, Sundays and Bank Holidays.

ABERDEEN – Aberdeen Art Gallery
Schoolhill, Aberdeen AB9 1FQ   Tel: 0224 646333
Friday 29th June 1990 – Saturday 28th July 1990
Open Monday to Saturday 10.00 a.m. to 5.00 p.m.
Thursdays 10.00 a.m. to 8.00 p.m.
Sunday 2.00 p.m. to 5.00 p.m.

Introduction – What is a Poem?

A Poem

Should every poem rhyme,
Each single boring line?
Or should the rhythm win,
And every word fit in?
Must it tell a tale?
Or will this method fail?
And how long should it be?
One line, two or three?
Or maybe this is wrong,
And a poem is . . .
A mass of ideas woven together,
With strands of imagination.
Sparkling moments,
incorporated into the beauty of the words,
thoughts and feelings,
creatively put together,
with a rhythmic metre,
words, bundled up into sentences
of fantasy,
a beginning, a middle,
and an end.

Nick Frew (11)
St Anthony's School, London

Me and My Family

June 14th, 1973

The sky was a luminous white.
A hawk circled, and then passed over in peace.
In the city there was an unusual silence
Almost as if everybody was at lunch.
An old woman sat on a public bench
Clutching half a bottle of meths.
Politicians rewrote the minutes of their last meeting.
Machines, cutting and slicing, churning and pounding,
Drowned human voices.
An army endured survival training.
Clocks stopped, started, and lost time
Making their owners late for work.
My mother fell asleep.
Everyone stopped short for a few seconds
And then carried on with life

On the day I was born.

Juliette Hollyman (15)
Ysgol Glan-y-Mor, Pwllheli,
Gwynedd

I saw my shadow

I saw my shadow on the wall,
I was tiny, but he was tall.
He wore black, but I wore red.
When the sun goes he'll be dead.
Shadow, shadow on the wall
Who's the fairest of them all.
You think you are so big and clever,
But I'm the one who stays forever.

James Logan (8)
St Andrew's School, Rochester,
Kent

I'm the smart one

I'm the one who stays home and studies.
I'm the one with posh clothes,
I'm the one who's going to get a job,
I'm the one who's picked on,
And joked upon.
I'm the one called 'Creep', 'Brain Box',
'Teacher's Pet'.
And I'm the one whose face is covered with spots,
And wears glasses,
I'm the one called 'Four eyes',
'Spotty',
'Wimp'.
I'm the smart one,
Or am I?

Mark Gaunt (14)
Windsor Park Middle School,
Uttoxeter, Staffs

Being black

I am black and you are white
You say I'm wrong and you are right
I'm just the same as you and you
I do the same I do, I do

To you I'm just a passer-by
And you still hate me, tell me why
I'm just the same as him and him
Every bone and every limb

Don't call me coloured it's not true
I am not green and I'm not blue
I'm just the same as them and them
I'm not a tiger or a wren

Let's not fight and let's be friends
Let's shake hands and make amends
I'm just the same as you and you
I do the same I do, I do

Rachel Gillies (11)
Nether Robertland Primary School,
Stewarton, Ayrshire

When I was three

When I was three I used to go to sleep
  on the stair.
My mum took a picture of me.
When I woke up I wondered where I was.
Later I saw this picture of me asleep
  on the stair.
I asked Mum to tell me who it was.

Sarah Cooper (7)
Havannah County Primary School,
Congleton, Cheshire
(Highly commended)

Bed time poem

Drinks and undress
Bed in a mess
Tinkles and teeth
Story and kiss
Good night sleep tight.
Don't let the bugs bite.

Pippa Carr (6)
Latchingdon, Essex

In bed

When I am in bed I hear
Footsteps of the night
Sharp like the cracking of a dead leaf in the
　　stillness
Then my mother laughs downstairs.

Idris Ghannan (8)
St Michael on the Mount School, Bristol

Stereotyped holly

Holly leaves have always been
Six prickles each and shiny green.
Until this year I looked again,
I thought them all to be the same.

A prickle here that's out of place,
A hooked nose on a matt green face.
An evil twist; a coloured ray,
An edge that's smoothed in a kindly way.

Holly leaves have never been
Six prickles each and just plain green.

Pamela Farries (15)
Castlegower, Castle Douglas

*'I would like to be a Punk
Rocker when I grow up'
Barry Todd (7)
Davington CP School,
Faversham, Kent*

The right to dream

Trains of cotton wool,
Dragging fleecy coaches through the feather trees.
From the window,
Here I look
Out to the ocean of rolling surf.
Here I'm dreaming of reality.
I'm breathing
But my heart's within my dream.
I live without life,
I move seven inches above the ground.

The ocean waves are lapping the shore,
The train floats on through misty air,
My eyes are shut,
But I can see
That no-one else is looking at me.
I'm no different,
I'm better here,
Better than I could ever be
But I have to return,
I have to accept,
I'm only as good as I was meant to be.

The ocean waves are lapping the shore,
The train floats on through misty air.
My eyes are shut
But I can see
That no-one can make me better than me.
I want everyone to see,
I've learnt my lesson,
I can now see,
There's no-one worse or better than me.
This is how I want it to be,
For everyone to see.

Sarah Green (12)
Streetly, Sutton Coldfield,
W. Midlands

Anger

My stomach is enflamed
My head fills with rage
My brain is in knots from the pain of it all

Everything around me turns to stone
Turns to stone with my anger

Rosemary Hayward (11)
Highfield School, Highgate, London

Another row

'How dare you say that to me?' Mam shouted.
Oh no, not another row.
'You can't boss me about,' I answered back.
'Yes I can.'
'No you can't,' I screamed,
'Wait till your dad comes home,' she said,
'Oh what does he know?'
'He knows a lot more than you that's for sure!'

Huh
'You're GROUNDED for a month,' Mam shouted,
'Oh good no school for a month.'
'That's it, you'll get sent to bed, with no supper.'
Oh, oh here comes Dad,
'Sorry Mam.'

Heather Middleton (9)
Sound Primary School, Sound,
Lerwick, Shetland

Two men punching

When my mum
tells me off
I get a feeling
like two men punching,
inside my throat.

Steven Smith (10)
Grasmere Primary School,
London

Asthma

I hate asthma
I get a dizzy head
And I feel sick and horrible
I take my asthma tube
I hate my asthma tube
The tablets are small and bitter
My mouth is all dried up
Like a wrinkled prune
I lie down
Then Dr Liston comes
He says Your lungs are expanding Debra
I said My lungs hurt so much

I get better.
I play out.
I say Good. I'm better!

Debra Maddison (8)
Portobello Primary School,
Chester-le-Street, Co. Durham
(Highly commended)

On me . . . as a dustbin

Sometimes I feel like a dustbin
Filled and ever filling
With things disposable
Junk food
Polluted air
Adults' opinions.
And I say
'STOP, STOP
You're filling me
Too full!'
And they say
'TOUGH'
And teach me
TRIGONOMETRY.

I want to know what happens
When I flip my lid.

?

Helen Goff (15)
Uxbridge, Middlesex

The chipper

Go roon' the corner, son
And buy twa haggis suppers.
Watch ye dinna scriff yer sannies
Or ye'll git mah slipper.
Here's the money, dinna lose it.
Remember what I said!
Now move it, or ye'll find
Ye'll gae up tae bed.

Now hurry, son, dinna dander.
Nae playin' wi' yer mate.
Come on now, son, watch oot
Or ye'll be too late.
'Sorry, son, nae haggis.'
That's what the chipper wifie said.
What will a say tae mah dad?
He'll put me to mah bed!

Ah suppose a'd better tak' a keek,
Through a windae at a telly.
There's a big puddle here
I'll splash in it wi' mah wellies.
So what if a git a row,
I'll be awa' tae scule.
A micht ride mah cartie i' the morn,
Or bunk aff an' play the fool.

Stephen West (11)
Longhaugh Primary School, Dundee
(Highly commended)

Eat it all up

The deep-purple slices just sit there,
Slimy and wet,
All the plate is empty
All except for those slices of beetroot
and my eyes fixed on them
Silence
I look up into those dark angry eyes.
And back
Back to the beetroot.
The clock ticks on
A great sigh of boredom breaks the quiet.
I pick up my fork
and stab into a slice
calmly.
As I lift the object
nearer my mouth
my nose begins to twitch
The smell crawls into my throat
making me swallow hard
trying to drive the foul taste
from my mouth.
The beetroot's getting nearer
Quick, I ram it into my
mouth and shut it fast.
I feel my throat tighten and gag
The taste poisoning my tongue
My eyes burn and widen
I grab for my glass.

I gulp some water down and try
  hard to swallow
My throat won't open, I push the
  chair from under me
  and run for the sink
My mouth explodes, leaving a mangled
  slice of beetroot.
I swill my mouth with water
trying to wash away the bitter taste.
I turn and face mother
The eyes glaring
She points me back to the chair
Back to the beetroot, then a
stubborn silence!

Amy Nicholls (13)
Sidcot School, Winscombe, Avon

'Natasha' Fiona Rawlinson (6)
South Green Infant School,
Billericay, Essex

Haircuts

Mum cut my hair. I hated that. First the front and then the back. It wasn't fair. I liked it long. I told her so, but she said, 'No.' I begged and cried to change her mind. Well now it's short, it looks O.K. Just wait till next year, I always say. I'll keep it long. Just you'd see. I only wish mum would leave it be.

Cam Phung Te (15)
St John Wall School, Handsworth, Birmingham

The poster

Daytime:
She is calm, still
In an everlasting pose
Just a poster of a lady
in black.

At night,
You have to look up
To see
not a silence – as before.
She compels you to stare
while hazy arms are gripped around her
pearly, precious neck.
And inside you she chokes
and screams
yet you are unable to help.

Hours in time later
tears, now damp on the pillow
have potioned you to sleep.
And while you dream
You know, deep within
that it was not she who choked
and screamed
But you.

Irene Anastassiou (14)
Notting Hill and Ealing High School,
Ealing, London

Pretty sure

I'm pretty sure it's at North View.
I'm pretty sure it's here.
I'm pretty sure it's in the wash.
I'm pretty sure it's in the loft.
I'm pretty sure it's with my ted.
I'm pretty sure it's in my bed.
I'm pretty sure it's in the drawer.

Are you pretty sure you're sure?
I'm pretty sure it's nowhere here.
I'm pretty sure it's nowhere there.
I'm pretty sure it's disappeared.
Are you pretty sure?
I am.

Jessica Michelson (9)
London
(Highly commended)

Confusion

Sweet, sweet hypocrisy!
Where does it start –
Where does it end?
In the head, or heart?

I hear one thing
Yet see another.
The idealist;
The socialist.

What is a socialist?
I know I've met them,
I've seen them act –
Yes, definitely act!

No, not just them.
The world is full of actors!
The more I see
I hope I just misunderstand.

I am no politician.
Neither could ever be;
Nor want to be.
I want to be innocent.

Prevailing innocence
Although I've seen it all.
That's exactly it –
I don't want to see it all.

So glasshouse stand forth –
Stones shall hit and miss,
I want the truth,
Yet I ask for a lie.

Linda Crook (16)
West Bridgford, Nottingham

'Gary' Emma Williams (14)
Denby, Derbyshire
(Highly commended)

Apology

I am sorry now
For all those things I do
(Biting my nails,
Mutilating orange juice cartons)
That I know
Annoy you.

I am sorry now
For all those things I don't do
(Rinsing out the bath,
Buying the drinks)
That I know
Irritate you.

I am sorry now
For all those things I say
(You don't have big ears
And you do wash up, occasionally)
That I know
Offend you.

I am sorry now
For all those things I will say
(Goodbye, I loved you,
The End)
That I know
Will hurt you.

I am sorry now
For all the things I don't say
(Should have done,
Would say, will do)
That I know
You could have done too.

Ellen Jackson (16)
Bristol, Avon

Strange new woman

She used to tell me how embarrassed she got.
She used to laugh and shake her hair until I'd die with
  not touching her.
She used to bite her nails until she gripped things and
  they hurt.
She and I were really happy.

She'd cry before exam results.
She always passed. I was always last.
We'd go out and drink coffee after school.
She and I were really happy.

She often liked to walk alone –
But not that often.
I'd wait until she returned, with the sun setting in her
  hair.

We'd not go out a lot, what
With wages being sparse.
I loved her, though,
Through all her difficulties.

Just recently she'd been away on
Holiday. Sad, I waved her smiling face goodbye
(I really did). Just yesterday
When she returned,
She brought with her a strange, new woman.

She frightens me.

Nina Couser (14)
Belfast

Outsider

Helen stands there empty,
Drained of happiness.
I stand in the corner,
Left out of family argument.
It's always like this,
Helen so precious,
A tiny white china doll.
I stand wondering,
We are so different,
Me, happy, free and boisterous,
Helen, silk, paints and porcelain.
Free Helen the caged dove,
She won't fly away.

Helen Milton (12)
Darrick Wood School, Orpington,
Kent
(Highly commended)

Reading

Reading slips past common reality
Each book, a miniature world I live in,
Absorbing pages like a thirsty sponge.
Dangers suffered with the characters-come-friends
Ideas revelling in my mind
Nailing me there, in suspense, till
Gently the last page flops over . . .

Lucy Howard (9)
New Malden, Surrey

Inside my head

Inside my head
Is a mist of description
For stories and poems.

A red carpet in Buckingham Palace
And the Queen announcing,
'This is the authoress, Gillian Buswell!'
Trumpets blow, the National Anthem is sung
And the dream fades as the dawn breaks in my mind.

I chew my pen and think,
'It's not fair, teacher, too much homework!'
Imagination takes over again,
I am at Woodside Vale, miles from anywhere,
Throwing breadcrumbs to the birds,
I am in Poland with Ania and Agnieska,
'Hocz Gillian, Ty jestesz gupja!'
Reluctantly I turn from their eager calls.
With a sigh to my homework,
'Too much, teacher, too much, too much . . .'

I think about Scrabble my hamster
And the roses in my garden,
Yellow mingles with pink and pink with red
As another picture forms.
I am at school playing 'Relievers'.
I can outrun everyone, I am a gazelle
Fleet and free, swift and happy.
Then my dad calls, 'Come on Gillian,
You need more exercise, lazy!'
Grunting lazily, I begin my homework poem . . .

Inside my head
Is a mist of description
For stories and poems.

Gillian Buswell (11)
Hutchesons Grammar
School, Junior School,
Glasgow

Shopping

I like shopping
I like buying
But when
I have no money
I am bored.
And I am moaning
And my mum
tells me off!
I drag behind
as slow as I can
till my mum said
'hurry up you'.

Thomas Pinnington (7)
St John's First School,
Norwich, Norfolk

Run the film backwards

It started on a piece of paper
in a poem, can't you see,
and now I'm getting smaller
instead of taller, this can't be.

I've stopped going on holidays
and my behaviour is getting worse.
I've started going on school trips
with a babyish little purse.

I'm getting more unfashionable
I've stopped attending school.
I'm going to kindergarten
wearing hats of wool.

Now I'm crawling around
like those things called dogs
and I've started playing
with things called golliwogs.

Now I only weigh 8lbs
the average they all say
I know I'm disappearing
will there be a yesterday?

Simon Reeves (14)
Crestwood School, Boyatt Wood,
Eastleigh, Hants

Putting my feet in cold water

Hot sticky feet
Quick quick
Off with my shoes
Cold water
Just waiting
When I put my feet
In, it stings and
Then it's lovely and cool
Weightless
I feel relaxed, and
My feet
Just aren't there.

Edward Thomson (11)
The Beacon School, Chesham Bois,
Amersham, Bucks

Excited

I

s
l
i
d
e

d
o
w
n

t
h
e

b
a
n
n
i
s
t
e
r
s

can't wait!

I ^{do}not ^{have} breakfast because I'm too
E X C I T E D

My arms S_HA^KE and S^HA_KE and S_HA^KE

My tummy TI^{CK}L_ES and TI^{CK}L_ES

O P E N   I T !

Mark Powell (7)
Nunnery Wood Primary School,
Worcester

A good little feeling

When I'm feeling glum
I think of lovely things instead
    of being grumpy
I think of a magic fairy that
    brings feelings.
Magic feelings! It's in my
    pocket.
My brother comes in and
    says who are you talking to?
Oh no-one! I've just got a
    Good Little Feeling!

Nina Miller (7)
Jordanhill School, Glasgow

My mother's bottom drawer

My mother's bottom drawer
Is full of wondrous things,
A tablecloth of Spanish lace,
A case of golden rings.

White stockings made of silk,
That my grandma used to wear,
Very ancient photographs
Wrapped with special care.

Old letters tied with ribbon,
A diary or two.
A box of pretty perfumed soap,
A scarf of Prussian blue.

Sometimes when I'm all alone
I like to curl up on the floor
And browse among the wonders
Of my mother's bottom drawer.

Natasha Williams (10)
St Andrew's School, Rochester,
Kent

My daddy

My dad goes away a lot
But he brings us presents back
He swings us upside down
And he goes to sleep
In front of the television.
Our dog takes him for a walk
Along the road,
His hair is black
He wears a pair of glasses
And as he strolls along
He pats me as he passes.

Felicity Campbell (8)
Fernhill Manor Junior School,
New Milton, Hants

'Me in My Yellow Wellies'
Alison Pickford (10)
Daven County Junior School,
Congleton, Cheshire
(Highly commended)

My brother Barry

He thinks he's a cool dude
In his winklepicker boots
And black leather coat.
His dark spiked hair
Makes him look like a hedgehog,
Red spots spangle
His chubby cheeks,
Everyone knows him better by
Monto.
He has a tough walk,
And an awkward run,
Always has three girlfriends
Not one.
You'd hear his car
In Timbucktoo
When he starts it in the morning,
He's no Elvis,
But to me, he's a star.

Glenn Montgomery (10)
St Mary's Primary School, Killyleagh,
Co. Down, N. Ireland

Nice girls

I have a cousin who's a 'nice girl',
She wears pink flowery dresses,
Which are never dirty,
Her doyley knee-length socks,
Match her underwear.

She can even eat brussel sprouts without looking ill,
And offers to do the dishes,
She keeps a lengthy diary,
Which her family read nightly.

Her mother chooses her boyfriends,
They're always polite,
And say 'please and thankyou'.

Every evening after her marmite on toast,
She does extra homework to please the teacher,
Then watches 'Blue Peter' and reads the *Guardian*.

Her friends are just the same,
Their pure white teeth,
And rounded, filed nails,
Free from dirt.

They return from play at 6 pm,
To climb the stairs to bed,
Where their mother kisses them goodnight,
And tucks them in.

But, before they go to sleep,
They read a chapter from the Bible,
And remember it!

Paul White (14)
Callington Community School,
Callington, Cornwall

Grandma

My grandmother lives with us,
We like to have her there,
She takes our Jack on the bus,
You wouldn't think she'd dare,
He always makes a fuss,
But Granny doesn't care.

Jessica Thorne (10)
Highfield School, Highgate,
London

Sleeping in my gran's house

Sleeping in my gran's house – it's horrid,
She keeps all the windows open,
It's toc cold to sleep.
And there's always a moth or two,
And even a spider.
The door slams shut,
A big gush of wind comes in,
Older people talking downstairs.
Her stairs creak loudly.

Carly Jones (10)
Penyrenglyn Junior School,
Treherbert, Rhondda,
Mid Glamorgan

Ship in a bottle

On Grandfather's sideboard,
Was a beautiful sight,
A ship in a bottle,
Shining so bright.

'Just sit down and watch it,
And one day you'll see,
Men preparing to sail,'
Said my grandad to me.

The ship had three sails,
A lifeboat on its side,
The nameplate was faded,
But it still longed to glide.

All day I observed it,
All time I ignored,
I too was observed,
By a sailor on board.

Julie Cooper (11)
Framlingham College Junior School,
Brandeston, Nr Woodbridge,
Suffolk

Unlucky

The grown ups are all safe,
Tucked up inside,
Where they belong.

They sit up reading,
Knitting,
And watching T.V.

We can enjoy ourselves now.
We can play in the backyards,
On all the lampposts,
In all the gardens,
And on all the shadows.

We're the cowboys against the Red Indians,
Squirting water everywhere,
Doing graffiti on the walls and pavements.
We're the British massacring the Germans
At the Second World War.

Then at ten thirty,
We can hear them coming,
Walking down the road.
Everything is still
Then someone runs to base.

They're after him!
All shouting 'Come 'ere you!'
And, 'Hey, it's time for bed!'
But we just shout 'Stuffit!'
And throw water bombs and rotten apples.
Eventually they overpower us.
We are prisoners of war!

Paul Heath (11)
Prebendal School, Chichester,
W. Sussex
(Highly commended)

'Self Portrait' Amelia White (17)
Albyn School for Girls, Aberdeen
(Italian Tour Award winner)

Ingredients for a Happy Christmas

One Nan and Grandad,
A large Christmas tree;
Mum, Dad, Brother,
And of course me.

A Turkey with stuffing,
A bottle of wine,
Carrots and Potatoes,
A short game of mime,

Liquor and Presents,
Wrappings ripped off,
Who gave me that?
Don't you dare scoff,

Oh, Thankyou Aunt Lilly,
I'll use it everyday,
Up to the cupboard,
Then put it away,

Nan and Grandad gone now,
Paper in the bin,
Mum's in the kitchen,
Resorted to gin,

Now it's all over,
James Bond on the box,
It's down to writing letters,
Thanks uncle for the socks.

Christian Lamb (13)
Lady Lumley's School,
Pickering, N. Yorks

Talking about School

sKooL

Ma wee sKooL,
Wis a guid wee sKooL,
But a left at summer term,
Tae go tae a sKooL,
That's a guid big sKooL,
With mair werk an stuff tae leurn.

Ma wee sKooL,
Wis a guid wee sKooL,
An a liked it affy well,
But everywan,
Wis gled tae heur,
The hof past three bell.

Ma new sKooL,
Is a guid big sKooL,
An it isna too bad,
Ma paw telt me,
That he went there,
When he wis a wee lad.

In a I'd say,
That baith the sKooLs,
Are jist aboot the same,
But everyday, I'm always gled,
Tae get oot o the place an go hame!

Jane Barrie (14)
Uddingston, Glasgow

Quick!

It's Monday school time,
But I think it is Saturday.
Mum says Quick Quick! It's Monday,
Oh does it have to be today.
It's the Swimming Gala you see,
She thinks she is not very good at it.

I get my swimming bag ready
Oh no! The talc's gone all over the floor,
Mum wipes it up then I go up-
Stairs and get ready.
It's nearly half past eight
And I'm going to be late.

Mum and I get in the car,
And drive to school
But when we get there
I want to go back home
Mum says no no you might
    Win.

Greer Stolton (7)
Hilden Oaks School, Tonbridge,
Kent

A teacher

Waking up at seven o'clock in the morning
is like rising from heaven, going to hell.
Who can dare say that this is a nine to five job?
Preparing my books and my lessons saving my energy
which is already like a cassette player.
I switch it on when I get to school
and off when I'm home.
I arrive at the zoo, boys barking and girls squeaking
Going inside the big cage, passing the zoo keeper's office.
What do I have planned today?
Oh yes a test! So a few hyenas won't be laughing.
Then there's a conference with the rest of the
Zoo keepers.
Followed by a quiet handwriting session
        It's Feeding Time!
At the sound of a bell it's freedom for the animals
and I've got peace of mind for an hour.
Dragging themselves back in – it's back to work
For them it's their favourite part of the day
For me it's deafness to the ears.
Out come the paints, my pet has lost his
painting, a bit like my patience.
A tiger and a lion fight at the back of the
classroom, and there are squabbles between
two cats.
Out comes the whip, but I dare not use it.
It may sound as if I hate this daily routine
but this is my chosen profession.
I'd rather be in this cage with harmless animals
Than out in the wild with dangerous creatures.

Harpal Dhaliwal (15)
Cranford Community School, Cranford,
Middlesex

Oh, my teacher!

Sorry Mrs Blewitt
I think I've lost my book
I don't know where I've left it
It might be on my hook.

Oh dear oh dear oh dear
I have to say Miss Mayer
I have tried and tried and tried
I will never be a netball player.

Sorry Mrs Childs
My birthday was last week
My daddy ate up all my cake
Wasn't that a cheek?

Mr Sinclair Mr Sinclair
Why are you so funny?
Is it all those Mars-bars that
Tickle in your tummy?

Michele Scopes (7)
West Hove Junior School, Hove,
Sussex

Shut up

He looked at me,
His nose wrinkled into a sneer,
His eyes bulged
Till they almost burst
And his mouth formed a straight line.

'What have you been doing?
Why are you so late?
This is the third time this week!
And I'm not very pleased!'

'So sorry sir,
Honestly
It's just that:
I couldn't find my toothbrush,
My sister chewed my work,
And I really couldn't eat the toast
It was horrid and burnt.
My shoes were in the coal hole,
And . . . .'

'Shut Up.'

Emma Mullen (10)
Highfield School, Highgate, London

Dissolving salt in water

The water sits still and pure
Then a sprinkle of dry white powder
Turns the water into a frothing mistiness
Who knows what lurks there?
The action of the spoon
When it moves the water
In goes the salt and makes a fizz
Causes a cloud like a puff of smoke
Slowly slowly they dance to the bottom
    of the jar
It disappears to a place far away
In goes more salt
It dances to the bottom
And disappears again
In goes more salt
It flows to the bottom
And stays there forever

Elizabeth Dyer (8)
Gaer Junior School, Newport, Gwent

Experiment

All eyes watching,
Faces tense.
Will it work?
The big event.
All are waiting,
Silent faces.
Then a bang!
Great Hurrayses!

But now we have to go and sit
And write something to go with it.

Katherine Fraser (12)
Richmond, Surrey

I hate writing poems

I hate writing poems.
I always seem to fail.
It feels like all my talents,
Are locked up in a jail.

When I try to rhyme my poems,
They never ever work.
And everyone at school,
Says that I'm er stupid.

everyone looks at me,
as though I'll get a fine.
if I forget to put capital letters,
at the beginning of a line.

I wish I could write poems,
I try so very hard.
But I know the windows on my jail,
Are definitely barred.

Michael Naylor (11)
Clifton Without Junior School, York

My poem!

There I am,
pencil in hand,
an empty notebook in front of me,
chewing my nails.
My friend shakes my shoulder.
Here, listen to this!
She reads her poem.
That's great,
I say.
Read me yours,
she says.
Miss's voice breaks in.
Come and sit on the carpet, children.

I'm not going to enjoy this.

Kate Gage (10)
Grasmere Primary School,
London

Origami

We were snaking along the road.
Everyone was rattling.
The teacher hissed 'Be quiet or we're never
going to get there.'
(We were going to our local library
to see a demonstration.)
'Do any of you know what origami is?'
'Yes Miss. It's self defence.'
'No! Do you know, Alec?'
'Origami. The art of paper folding.
It originated in Japan.'
'Smart Alec!
Here we are. The library and our origami demonstration.
You may sit. Fold your arms.'
Funny. I thought it was paper
we were meant to be folding!
The man giving the demonstration had fingers
as agile as an acrobat
as he twisted and turned the paper.
The folds in the paper matched my brows!
Well, as you can imagine
when we had a go we were in a flap . . .
never mind the bird.
Then it was all over.
We headed back to school.
Inspired we were.
Trouble was, by the time we got back
we'd forgotten most of it.
The birds had flown!

Emma Cooper (11)
Cloudside County Junior School,
Sandiacre, Nottingham

Some People

Jigsaw

Some people are incomplete
like an unfinished jigsaw
A picture left imperfect.

Some make their own piece
to fill the gap
Improvising with their 'artistic' eye.
Others are clever
they smile and laugh
letting their twinkling manner guide a
probing eye away.

But many just
lie broken.
Gaping,
Waiting and hoping
someone will find the last piece for them.

Magda Hewitt (16)
Billericay School, Billericay, Essex
(Highly commended)

The introvert

Strip off this dull covering
and gaze intently
at the blank, brown packaging.
This gives no clue
to its glorious content.
Nothing exudes from
this seemingly empty skin.
It gives no evidence
of the sweet perfume within.

Claire Ginn (16)
Billericay School, Billericay, Essex
(Highly commended)

'Nude Etching'
Helen Lake (17)
Stockport
Grammar School,
Stockport,
Cheshire
(Special mention)

Pointing

The woman is thin
Pointing to what could be
Anything, up in the sky
Pointing with all her body
Her feet
Her waist
Her hair
All the way up to her finger
Large and motionless.

What is she pointing at
Nobody knows
Her expression shows
Want and need facing upwards.
Her dress long and thin
Her hair hanging, poised
Waiting for something to happen.
Something terrible?
Something wonderful?
Something historic?
Something special?

Her hands were
Big and lumpy,
One pointing
One clutching her heart.

Sophie Rickard (9)
Whalley CE Primary School,
Whalley, Blackburn, Lancs

Faces

Little
Sally
Drake

Leans against the peeling wall
And stares out.

No substance; no thought; no room
To manoeuvre the State, the Party –
Huxley, Orwell, Toffler.

That faceless Face,
That straight linearity.

'Conform to rules. Stay within the lines
And you'll be O.K.
In your inexorably shrinking cage,'
They said.

But
Little Sally
Drake

Does not want to conform.
She looks for another dimension,
A higher plane

On which to think,
To brood; to ferment her fury
Within her sad eyes.

Samir Satchu (16)
The King's School, Canterbury,
Kent

Cassie

Cassie's mum cleared out
long ago.
Her dad doesn't have
the time.
She lives on her own
on the
council estate.
On Friday night Cassie's dad
doesn't come home at all.

She seems lonely,
I asked
her to
come round, said she didn't
have the time.
And to make it worse she's
in our
Teacher's Bad Books. She just
wears denim
to school all the time.
It hardly ever gets washed.

Cassie gets picked on for
being last.
Cassie gets laughed at for
getting it wrong.
'CASSANDRA DAVIS'
stand in the corner.
Poor CASSIE.

Then on Thursday when
Cassie
was walking home from
school
her mum drove past in a
BMW,
And said 'Cassie get in
the back' and she did.
They
drove away and that was the
last
of Cassie.
Cassie was gone.

Emma-Kate Lidbury (8)
Cricklade, Swindon, Wilts

'Friend' Chloe Steers (17)
King Edwards School,
Bath, Avon

Feet

Her hairy feet
Were in horny sandals,
She had a flowing dress
And a nosy smile.
Funny, toes with square ends.
When she was talking
She pressed her face close,
Till I could see each
Coarse grey hair
On her chin.
Her toenails were yellow.
She shut one eye
And stroked a hand
Down a prickly leg,
Where great veins fed
A fat mole in the hollow of her ankle.

I tried to answer her questions
But I kept looking at her feet.

Katie-Louise Thomas (16)
Chelsfield, Kent
(Italian Tour Award winner)

Vegetable versification

I've fallen in love with the veg. man
He's saved my life once again.
I was s'posed to go down to the grocer's
Even though it was pouring with rain.

Me hair was all of a muddle
Me nail varnish not quite dry.
I had to do something, and sharpish
Then his shining white van did I spy.

It's head-over-hills with the veg. man
I think it was love at first sight.
He said 'Wada ya want? an' 'ow much?'
Then, 'Luv, a' y' feelin' alright?'

Me knees were all of a quiver
On the whole I felt quite ill.
My voice it 'ad gone all wobbly
An' then he gave me the bill.

The way that he passed it over
With his hands so mucky and strong.
The mean gaze leaving his eyes
Was enough to turn any girl on.

Once I was home and recovered
Made myself a nice cuppa o' tea.
I decided to go to our Mabel's
To see when his next round would be.

She told me he *came* round on Sundays
Though 'cos of a change in the law
He only comes round on a Friday now
So's I probably won't see him much more.

By gum, this news did distress me
I could only see him once a week.
And then, whenever he did appear
I hadn't the nerve to speak.

Mind you, it did save me me lolly
Couldn't afford to see him every day.
Apples bananas and peaches
Lay in his van in array.

I couldn't resist the temptation
To ask for that little bit more.
I hated the moment he left me
And closed that veg. van's white door.

In three weeks I'd turned to a veggie
In all senses of that sacred word.
I lived for Friday mornings
When the noise of his van could be heard.

I got through ten tonnes of tomatoes
Eight carrots at breakfast I had
Along with peas, lettuce and brussels,
Enough to send any girl mad.

I *was* madly in love with the veg. man
But now he's ruined me life.
I 'aven't seen him for three weeks y' see
'Cos he's gone off to Spain with his wife.

I've chucked out me onions and spinach
Me spuds and me oranges too
I've become a regular 'uman
Though I'm feeling a bit down and blue.

A changed girl, a meat-eating person
Done with me pepper and pear
You should see the new bloke at the butcher's
For him I could now really care.

Tracey Thomas (15)
Holme, Peterborough, Cambs

The nature of man

A jug of chemicals
for an interview?

He lined himself,
as a bowerbird does his nest,
to better his rival.

Only to be ranked
as chickens
and twisted
like an ivy.
To creep along
the chosen wall.

Claire Davis (13)
Newcastle-under-Lyme School,
Newcastle-under-Lyme, Staffs
(Arthur Lines Poetry Award
winner)

Tolerance

We sat beneath a summer dawn
Waiting for warmth to creep like
A shadow upon our frail bodies,
And when at last we had thawed
From the cloudless, icy night,
Each looked into the other's eyes
And saw the frost, lingering still
As it always had, and we knew
It would remain, unchanged from
Day to monolithic day; but we
Stayed together to speak in
Monotones of polite hatred
As we always had, for we
Preferred this to loneliness.

Claire Pearson (17)
Sidcot School, Winscombe, Avon.

'Mr Hyde'
Stephen Callaghan (7)
Merrylee, Glasgow

Corset and combinations

Combinations tends the rose beds,
Mounds the earth and snips at the grass,
Corset meanwhile starches the curtains,
Vinegars the windows, picks the roses for her class.

Combinations potters in the potting shed,
Measures the nail on which to hang his secateurs,
Corset's eye spies through the latticed window,
Lifts her chin, drops her eyes, sniffs in sharp and briskly
    stirs.

Combinations lifts his watch and wanders down the path,
Wobbles the wobbly fencepost and shows some mild
    concern,
Corset switches pinny from the plain to the poppied one,
Dishes up sprouts and beans and broccoli to each plate in
    turn.

They must be in there, somewhere,
Carefully eating, everything fine,
Never seen, unheard, secretly pinning
Corsets and combinations on the line.

Katie-Louise Thomas (16)
Chelsfield, Kent
(Italian Tour Award winner)

The rivals

He was still there
Crouching over the regimental rows of Begonias
In the half light.
Some people said he was obsessed.
He could not feel her watching him,
But only the lingering dampness in the evening air
And the sweet perfumed companionship of the Roses.
She tried to remember a time
When he had touched her
The way he touched their silken petals.
She wanted to tear the head
From each self-satisfied bloom
And crush it in her hand,
Until it was just a velvet pulp.
Perhaps then he would look up at her,
Into her face,
And listen as his battalion of shrubs cried out
In silent distress –
'It was your wife who destroyed your garden.
Your jealous wife
Who has only flowers to despise.'

Kathryn Simmonds (16)
Digswell, Welwyn, Herts
(Highly commended)

The chainmaker

With well-worked hands he wields the hammer,
Bringing down the heavy tip,
Shuddering the forge with echoing, hollow notes,
Metal against the anvil.

Held in the tongs the soft, hot metal is pliable like
    melted toffee,
Curved to mathematical perfection,
Smouldering dimly in the heat of the fire,
Plunged hissing into water.

Behind him the chain grows,
A monster, snake's body twisting, its head white-hot in
    the fire.
A skill practised by generations,
Link by link.

Hannah Pennell (10)
Settle, N. Yorks

'Two Firemen' Giselle Crossan
& Emma Love-Lowry (10)
Pycroft Middle School,
Chertsey, Surrey

He was rooted

He was rooted
like the oak.
The weather changed
in his veins.
His ears heard the
first phlegm-rattled gasp
of a womb-warm lamb.
His sharp, blue eye
admired Spring's first bud,
gentle as his hands
persuading the udder.
His wind-worn voice
calmed the cow.
His kingdom of
rhythmic fields
was shaped by his love.

Now, his sons are men
with new ideas.
The droning of their machines
drowns the lamb.
Their hedge-cutter slices
the untidy bud.
Their milking machine
forces the udder.
His acres are
shaped by straight wire.

His voice is old.
The oak is hacked
from its roots.

Elen Jones (17)
Ysgol Glan-y-Mor, Pwllheli,
Gwynedd

'*Harlequin and Partner*'
Susan Anderson (17)
The Park School, Glasgow
(Italian Tour Award winner)

Frozen Ps and Qs

Normal Bowel Movements
For a man his age
Not bad, in fact quite spritely.

More Council Complaints
For weather like this
One outside lav for ninety

A Long Journey
For nature's call and sanctuary
From snow storms blowing nightly

Cold Blue Legs
For inadequate nightwear
Wellies hang loose looking unsightly

Almost Journey's End
For the wind whistles up his passage
Too much trouble just to go fortnightly

People Stand Huddled
For the crowd around the loo is long.
He holds his little pink roll tightly

His Turn Now,
For a long and tiring wasted journey
Another false alarm.

One day he'll never make it back.

Fiona Beresford (15)
Middlecroft School, Stavely,
Chesterfield, Derbyshire

Wales

The traditional Wales –
Rows of houses
Clinging to hills,
Dreary coal wheels
Against a picturesque background.

The fighting Wales –
A red dragon,
Protecting its property,
Its fiery breath
Destroying every summer house in its path,
Proclaiming that Wales is not for sale.

My Wales –
Streets littered
With chewing children
And bargains,
Perm-headed girls
Drinking beer and smoking,
An ordinary world.

Anna Daniel (13)
Ysgol Tryfan, Lon Powys,
Bangor, Gwynedd
(Highly commended)

Country people

A cartoon of two brothers.
Haggling with the pavement.
Each step a price to reach town.
One always followed behind
Like a faithful hound
They never 'rode' together.
John is the elder brother –
His hat is thatched a darker brown
And his eyes are indifferent
To my youth as I rush to school.
I adore their ages because smiles
From the old are young.
Their warmth is endless as time.
The youngest always beams to me, his dinner
Locked in between his dentured teeth.
I remember our first encounter
With those shire-horse hands.
As rough as the land they once furrowed.
There seemed to be echoes of hens
in his voice, as Glyn paged through the album.
Hills, sheep and the warm teats of cows
Were their hardest sacrifice to a town life.
Like Three Musketeers they live
Glyn, John and Cadi
All for one and one for all.
Cadi is an eternal Christmas –
Her hands always glove my own
And she takes me to the kitchen –
To the pickles and bottled chutney
and the rhubarb and fruit cakes.
The room is a museum of aromas.
I love how sage hangs like a bat
In the pantry – asleep until Sundays.

Sometimes they all three waved
'Yohooing' above the fence.
And I'd go as to the church altar –
A communion awaits.
And the bread and wine are gifts.
Fresh potatoes, cox apples or sweets.
We give too but they give harder.
One without the other is a
Chain with a broken link.
But Glyn broke away via a stroke
And the pool of the eyes set in.
John drags to the town today
With only his shadow
As a ghost behind him.
His partner walks only to the window
and his language comes from the eyes.
On my way home from school I notice
The dancing of the curtain in his room
And the arcing of lips in a smile.
He speaks to me with the tongue of
His hands.

Bethan Roberts (17)
Ysgol Glan-y-Mor, Pwllheli,
Gwynedd

Sad Stories

An apple a day

You spy me.
I sit between an orange and a large, fat, juicy pear.
Elbowed out of the way by a thin, moulding banana.
You have found my hiding place at last.
You take me from my fruitbowl home,
rub me on your sleeve until my tight coat glows
    invitingly,
I have seen it happen to others; I know what's coming
    next.
You begin to flay me, strip off my skin, slowly,
in long curls of blood-red.
I burst out, hard, white and cold from my jacket.
I lie, in your mercy, on the hard, flat chopping-board.
There is nowhere to hide, no escape from the sharp,
    silver blade.
You hold the knife, cruel, gleaming with delight in the
    sunshine.
I utter one last, small, hopeless prayer and close my
    eyes . . .

Alison Legge (13)
Newcastle-under-Lyme School,
Newcastle-under-Lyme, Staffs

Listening to sad music

The music is like someone
                    crying
Because they have no one
            to play with.
A sea bird is dying
Because it is trapped in
                some oil
Or a ship is sinking under
                the sea.
It is some gold dust glittering
            in the moon light
Or a tree being cut down
    which has lived for a million
        years
Or longer.

Richard Beaumont (7)
Shottermill County First School,
Haslemere, Surrey
(Highly commended)

Out of her depth

In Summer's scorch
The sea is cold.
Strangely sensuous
Caressing
Repressing
Disjointing limbs.
Draining colour.
Sand welcomes
Tentative tread.
Suddenly
Carpet melts.
Splintering glassy calm
She plummets
Down . . .

Snorting spheres
Wording the silent shriek,
Then exploding
In a maelstrom,
Spluttering spit,
Breathing brine,
Plunging back
Further
Down . . .

Tortuous torture.
An eternal second,
Suspended
Spiralling,
Like a paperweight,
Fleshy conch,
Life locked
In glass.

Eyes strain upwards.
Gasping,
Grasping
At strings
Of sunlight.
Then smashing through
The shivering mosaic
With a fist,
Shattering
Scattering pieces.
Fingers scrabbling
At the violet vault,
Slippery smooth.
Lungs splitting
Screaming
For breath.
Then tumbling
Stringless puppet,
Wingless bird,
Down
Down
Down . . .
The sea
Unmoved
Unmoving
Save a
Tittering turbulence.
Then still.
The sea is cold.

Rosanna Lowe (16)
Kenilworth,
Warks

Prostitute

Petals of the flower
Part revealing white
    uneven teeth.
Her lips were deliciously
Smug in red,
I want her, the men said.
(But I wanted her.)
She had a baby, they said,
Brown it was, touch of the
Tarbrush, they said.
(I loved her baby.)
She cried only once,
like a dull shower of
Rain over her teacup.
Stupid cow, they said
Was always complaining
She never slept.
Now she sleeps alone and
    Cold.
And I cried at the funeral,
Holding her
Brown Baby.

Giovanna Iazzi (15)
Trinity Catholic High School,
Woodford Green, Essex

Victim of the night

Footsteps . . .
Behind, following,
Muffled and hollow.
Sweat breaks out.
He glances about him
Nervously.
A voice mutters,
Stifled in the night sounds,
His pace
Quickens.
The vultures move,
A kill is sensed.
The shadow behind
Grows closer,
Closing in.
Another appears,
A silhouette by a lamp.
Then another,
Blocking his way,
He panics.
A pause . . .
Then he runs!
Down a dark alley he stumbles,
His fear forces him on.
A knife flashes,
A cry of fear.
He slumps down.
A victim of the night.

John Plunkett (14)
Wymondham High School,
Wymondham, Norfolk

The gun

Cold and evil,
Still it lay,
Waiting for an owner,
To take it in his hand,
Shiny black steel,
An oily finish,
And a glowing ebony handle,
Hide the monster beneath.

The owner came,
Only just an adult,
Juvenile and boyish,
To flip it in his hand.
Gratitude flows through the gun,
The terrible monster is risen.

Richard Cull (12)
Bracknell, Berks
(Highly commended)

A poster on the wall: 1914

A poster parades a foreign adventure,
Uniform, pay and everything free,
A rifle to sling across your shoulder,
The glory of protecting your great country.

Now the adventure begins,
A foreign land awaits,
A chorus of voices sing,
As they anticipate,
A valiant Christmas victory,
Backpacks all in order,
Rifles gleaming in the midday sun,
Shining boots like mirrors,
Naive human cannon fodder,
Lined up one by one.

First arrival in France,
Streets are lined with maids and men,
Most of them give joyful cheers,
The knowing ones shed silent tears,
As the fighters continue under marching orders,
The path they take is painfully long,
But across the Franco-Belgian border,
As they approach the Angels of Mons,
Joyful faces and cheerful welcomes,
Are now all but gone.

Peasants are hidden in their houses,
The marching songs begin to die,
Pensive privates try to sleep,
Bivouacked beneath a blood red sky,
No soft warm bed,
A khaki blanket,
Cold hard ground as a mattress,
Morale goes down with the sun,
But still the poster says,
Death to the evil Hun.

As a new day begins,
A schoolboy-soldier's life ends,
After a black-crossed eagle
Spits lead at him from the sky,
And mesmerized masses stare
At his mutilated body on the dirty ground,
The field grey enemy,
Is no longer across the sea,
The suspense and the waiting,
Will only last a few more hours.

Hell finally arrives,
The poster on the wall somehow disappears,
Will anyone survive,
This bloody sea of mud,
A field grey advance,
A khaki retreat,
Targets at a fairground.
King's shilling per go,
A glorious, victorious dream,
Turns into a muddy nightmare,
. . . And in the midst of it all a poster lies in shreds on
   the bloody ground.

Paul Corcoran (14)
Burnham Grammar School,
Burnham, Nr Slough

How gloriously soldiers always die

Black flags and shirts from every Irish window are hung
   out
To greet the funeral train that slowly fights
A way past graffiti and shut-up shops.
The feet of 'mourners' scrunch in broken glass like
   rifle-fire,
And scuff the carboned road like police-radios.
The wind dare not blow,
But rain hisses.

But in France, sheets of starch-white paper shone brightly
Against notice-boards, scarred by pins,
Like a strategic scale-model of No-Man's Land.
A man passed, counting casualty lists already soaked by rain
And stolen for letters.

The crowd shoves and pushes
The people along the breaking street,
And it knows that somewhere up ahead
There bobs a coffin.
Inside a boy lies, dead.

'How many?' someone asked from the dankness of damp
   dug-out.
'Only fifteen,' the soldier said.
Some post-men passed, struggling under
The letters of fifteen hundred dead.
Rain fell, water dripped, and men did not sleep.

Babies cry, so mothers push prams
Whilst brothers push drugs on the kids next door;
They move away to scrounge for a fag, and
Sit in trees like the village elders, drinking from
    coke-cans,
And hating with their mouths . . .

The men lay in water and cursed the weather and fought it
    with sandbags,
And Generals sat behind desks watching rain, and cursed it,
And fought it with letter-openers.
At home people queued through puddles
And cursed.

– They hate fat, beef-chewing, beer-gulping Protestants,
And thin, sadistic Mr Average Brit,
Who shot in the back, and murdered good Catholics,
And the kids next door who got more pocket-money, and
    had a television.

Men looked at new neighbours and sighed;
Generals subtracted deaths and added new recruits and
    sighed
And sent frantic letters;
Young black-cloaked widows stared at little brown
    telegrams,
And cried.
Nights would fall, and all would be quiet save
For the blowing of poppies in the breeze.

A woman is near the coffin;
Her son would have liked the funeral,
She thinks, as she cries silently in the silence.
She does not hear the vicious chants of
People who know not what they mean,
Or the reason why he died.

I look at the simple concrete cross,
And see the tattered red-stained cardboard of a poppy
wreath.
I look for some inscription to record some hero's name,
But all the words that I can find are
'Lest we forget those who died   Lest we forget those who
died'.

I ask 'What was his name?'
'Whose name?' a man replies.
'The boy who's dead, in the coffin up ahead,' I say.
He shrugs and turns, and says not a word.

DULCE ET DECORUM ERAT PRO PATRIA MORI

Toby Brown (16)
The King's School, Canterbury,
Kent
(Highly commended)

Remembrance Day

As two minutes start many people freeze,
to remember the dead, injured and maimed.
An old man stops moving his wheelchair,
to remember his friends, dead, injured – to remember
   when he
Could walk, the fun he had running, jumping – frozen by
   a thin piece of iron.
The men who survived the blazing skies thinking of
   those not quite so lucky.
They are dead, but why, what is the reason, nobody
   knows.

Gavin Wilkins (11)
Thomas A'Becket Middle School,
Worthing, West Sussex

'Pieta'
Richard Press (17)
Lockleaze Secondary
School, Bristol, Avon
(Highly commended)

Desolation

For four weeks and four days,
I had wearily trudged through the snow
ahead I had to go,
battling with the frost.
The paths were hidden,
I felt like giving up,
I knew I was lost.

Twice I collapsed,
buried in the snow,
But trying to keep warm.
I tried to conjure up my wife's loving warm face,
Our cosy red brick place, back home.

It was war that started this,
War, bombs, Hitler.
'War!' I shouted. And then 'Peace!' 'War'
'Peace' the mountains echoed around me.
Then I saw a light, a flicker.
I gave a cry and stumbled
to the ground,
towards the light, but then it flickered
Off into the night.
But I knew which way I had to go,
no longer I heeded the snow.

One hour later,
I was there.
I stood and stared.
Tears pricked my eyes.
But I was not surprised.
But I had expected this,
I wasn't surprised.

I peered into each hole, and slum,
Families were sitting pale faced,
Staring into outer space.
Then I saw a woman I knew. She was a friend, who
knew about my wife and family.
I pumped her for news.
She turned away. She did not have much to say.

'The children?' I asked fearing the worst.
She turned around, and let out a slight curse.
'Your wife,' said she, 'in the middle of the night was
    taken away from her family, to work.'
'The children?' I asked. 'They had a terrible fright.
They were taken afraid.
In the middle of the night there was a bomb raid.
They are gone.'
I turned my back on her.
Her words echoed in my head.
'They are gone gone gone.'
I buried my face in my hands.
All this for nothing.
Gone, Gone, Gone.

Clare Norris (10)
Albert Primary School, Penarth

I'm scared

I'm scared
The throng is loaded into the car,
like dirt being shovelled into a hole.
We fill the gaps and consume
the sticky, smelly, sweaty air.
Buttonholes of light struggle into the crowded, noisy car.
Where is my family?

I'm scared
There's my Mother, paralyzed by her pride.
She will not let salty tears stain her dirty face.
We're trapped like beasts in a cage.

I'm scared.

Nea Bayley (14)
John Kyrle High School, Ross-on-Wye,
Herefordshire

'Open Door' Pamela Cartwright (16)
Newcastle Emlyn Comp School, Newcastle Emlyn, Dyfed
(Highly commended)

Front page picture

Death in Northern Ireland. Two points of view.

View One

PHOTOGRAPH BY . . .

Me.
I took the picture,
The corpse lying in the mud,
Gunfire still ringing in my ears,
Buzzing through the picture –
CLICK.
Tears wetting the cheeks of a new widow,
The bewildered eyes of a fatherless son,
Innocent.
Looking at me through the picture.
CLICK.
News to the ignorant world.
Not softened by pages of words –
Clear, plain for the world to see.
And didn't they love it?
CLICK.

View Two

The shot that killed a man,
Just a muffled bang.
The grenade from someone's hand,
Just a small puff of smoke.
The corpse, lying savagely beaten and shot,
Just somebody's son.
That shot that killed that man,
Frozen, preserved, cold but real,
That grenade from the unknown hand,
Halted, stripped down to the bones of hate,
That corpse, lying, robbed of all pride,
Trapped in time, helpless.
Fold up the newspaper.
Hide it away.
Go up to my room and cry for the
Man without a face:
My son.

Catherine Clarke (10)
Rothwell, Kettering, Northants

Ulster August 1988

The carcass of a bus
Lies pitifully in the street
Surrounded by flowers.
The charred cap
Of a young soldier
Rests untouched
In the street,
Another victim of the butchers
Whose excuse is their country.
Their sport is the killing
Of innocent people.
They terrorize
To fight for their freedom,
Ha,
Cowards,
Who use their tear-stained history
For an excuse to kill.

Samantha West (14)
Sevenoaks, Kent

The Game

Arson
Hurt none
Your brother's keeper
Not you, half-sister
Loads carried you lighten
Eternal flame his
No crime
Yours

Mind
Still warped
Unable to stop
Mesmerized: open flame
Bright light leaping higher
His portfolio
One month
Prison

Imagine
(She answers)
Events as a game
The game is burnt Death
Match in trembling
Reverent fingers
Strike one
Ablaze

Corinne Berg (13)
Newstead Wood School for Girls,
Orpington, Kent

Oor hoose

Today da day dat dey cum and turn us oot.
Dey ha cum fae hell.
Da factor cums wi tree chaps.
Dey cum tae trow us oot of oor hoose
We left a part o us in oor hoose.
Der was a procession dat slowly moved along.
I looked back at oor hoose as we went over da hill.

Our house

Today's the day that they come and turn us out.
They have come from hell.
The factor comes with three men.
They come to throw us out of our house
We left a part of us in our house.
There was a procession that slowly moved along.
I looked back at our house as we went over the hill.

Russell Pottinger (11)
Hamnavoe School, Burra Isle,
Shetland

The castle

Rough people and horses dying
People in the dungeons with no food
Judges shouting, people dying for food
But the other knights won't listen.
Knights keep judge of the dungeons
So the people can't get out.
Girls do the work, the work is this,
Washing, scrubbing the walls
Tidying the room and the table
Much more than you do at home
You don't scrub the walls
Some lucky dungeon people get water to drink
But still no food.
No-one gets food in the dungeons.
The knights get food brought out to them.
When it is bed time dungeon people
Have to sleep on the hard ground
And no covers.
Then breakfast time knights eat
Stuffed dormice, birds, meat and spices.

Mahala Dawson (7)
Leeds

Trial by mountain

The peak soared above him, a rocky lance jutting into the
　　sky

His lacerated palms gripped tightly on the lip of the
　　ledge, knuckles white

Flames spurred through his hands, but Joh would not die,

Would not let go, would not fall from this mountainous
　　height.

He glanced down, saw only mist and grey-white clouds,
　　and he knew

That to let go meant death shattered amongst the rocks,
　　a grim fate for a grim task

But it was not to be: For deep in his heart he knew what
　　he must do.

And as he dangled from the brim of the ledge his face
　　became a mask,

Sour with hate.

　　　Hate for orcs, he remembered, the foul daemons of
　　　　filth,

　　　Hate for the priests of Redeye, for his lightless days
　　　　of pain,

　　　Hate for Halcyon the rat and his leech, a deathless
　　　　devouring sylph

　　　There was hate, and sorrow, and pain that was not
　　　　feigned.

　　　And from this hate he drew out some inner strength,
　　　　some power divine,

　　　Perhaps even the hand of some benign god touched
　　　　him at that moment,

　　　So he grimly pulled his exhausted body up; for he
　　　　had no time to pine,

　　　No time to rest, only to continue, to carry out his
　　　　skyward ascent

　　　To heaven.

The climb was pain, pain more searing than any Joh had
  felt before,
But he would not falter, he would not stop, that he
  knew,
For he had not come this far to die on a peak so full of
  hidden lore:
His quest was for the mallorn-tree; for in the skies legend
  foretold it grew,
With it lay the fabled Windsword from the ancient world
  of old –
This alone was worth the pain, the suffering, for it held
  the power
Over life, over death, over his future: to him it was more
  than gold.
Joh Windsword resumed his climb; for he was
  determined to conquer this tower,
And fight on.

'Seven magic tasks
To pierce any soul
On the island
Of the sons of Zar
Beware thyself!'

John King (11)
Alvechurch Middle School,
Alvechurch, Birmingham

Royal execution

Six red sapphires
On snow white silk
Deadly music heard
And a glint of silver.

Joanna Smith (10)
Canterbury, Kent

'Working at Home (Wednesday Feeling)'
Eva Arrighi (17) Govan High School,
Glasgow (Italian Tour Award winner)

His life and hers

I know a girl who's anorexic.
She vomits night and day.
I know a boy who isn't,
But he's dying anyway.

She longs to be a model,
Slim and slender as they say;
He longs to have plump arms and legs,
But he's dying anyway.

She haunts herself with visions
Of buttocks as they sway;
He's revolted by his body,
But he's dying anyway.

He sits amongst the shadows
Trying to recall his life,
But all that he remembers
Is hunger, drought and strife.

She's obsessed with thoughts of weight and size
Her whole life is a mass of lies;
He longs for love, and food and care:
She's crying as he's dying.

Frances Maclennan (12)
Hewett School, Norwich,
Norfolk

The mission

A small, thin, emaciated Ethiopian
Went wandering one day;
He came wandering out of his land of hunger,
He wandered right out of the misery,
And stumbled over continents,
Stumbled through rich, green fields
And could not understand.
He waded through rivers of clear water
And could not understand.
Eventually, he came to a silent city:
He saw an old man trudging through the streets,
The man was afraid.
He saw a young child
Tottering in the dust.
The child was afraid.
The African carried on through the empty roads;
He came near to two, tall, iron gates,
Clamped with a padlock,
But as he approached, the padlock sprang open.
The gates were wide open, welcoming him in.
He went through a courtyard filled with dying trees
And into an office;
Tired, frightened men in pin-striped suits,
Laid their heads on the desks in weary submission.
The starving man went on, unafraid
A brown, shrivelled figure
Incongruous in this world of luxury.
Past blank television screens,
Secretaries, frozen over their typewriters.

He came to a reinforced steel door
With strange words written in red paint.
The man from the other world,
The other century,
Again, the doors opened
And the man walked through,
Guided by a Power
Who had compelled him to do this thing –
To exterminate mankind
So that the world could start again,
The bellies of the starving could be filled,
And the powerful could learn humility.
He came to a panel
Where a single, red button sat in the middle
He raised one, brown finger . . .

Elizabeth Gowing (15)
Malvern Girls School, Malvern,
Worcs

Starvation

With this song I'm gonna rap the nation,
People in Africa are dying of starvation,
I think it's my occupation
To give them all a dedication,
And stop all the aggravation.

CHORUS   So come on put your hand in your pocket,
Even if you have to sell your locket.

Please help to save the nation,
Because they're in a vital situation,
There won't be a complication,
If you give a dedication,
To people who are dying of starvation.

CHORUS   So come on put your hand in your pocket,
Even if you have to sell your locket.

CHORUS   Even if you have to sell your locket
So come on put your hand in your pocket.

Donna Lewis (13)
Etone School, Nuneaton,
Warwickshire

Sonnet

Come rain and wash the sins of man from earth
With soft sweet water falling from the skies,
Your droplets have caressed our cheeks since birth
And mingled with the tears that flow from eyes.
Now purge this land of all our evil deeds.
Drive out the hate and anger from within.
With tender love awake the sleeping seeds
And so command a new life to begin.

As humans we presume we own the world,
We fight, and wound and murder fellow men,
And even when the mercenaries grow old,
A younger generation start again.
So come now, rain, and with your soothing touch
Restore to us the love we need so much.

Catherine Richards (16)
St Mary's School, Ascot,
Berkshire

Saved

They locked him up
For what he thought;
They locked him up
For what he said
And for believing
And knowing
What was right
And good.

Because he had warned them
They locked him up
In the deepest
Of deep cells
Where nothing could reach him
Or even get near.

They locked him up
Because he said,
'They know not what they do.'
And, knowing,
Or not knowing,
They did it.

They pressed the button
The explosion killed many;
The blast even more
But the greatest evil
Hung like a non-moving cloud
Turning
Dust
To dust
And from the dust
The prisoner walked free.
He had not meant
To save himself.

Tim Connors (12)
Debenham High School,
Debenham,
Stowmarket, Suffolk

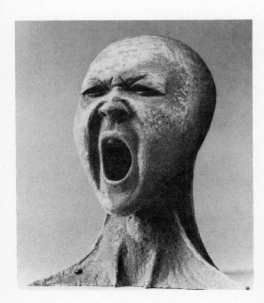

'The Scream'
Scott Shepherd (17)
Buckhaven High School,
Buckhaven, Fife
(Highly commended)

107

The painter's dream

You fall from grace like tears from a child.
Your blue, blue eyes, your hair dark and wild
with your sense of adventure and paints in your hand
you travel along and live off the land. Beauty you capture
   with the stroke of your brush
And the rhyme in your heart which you quote in a rush.

Cause people to dismiss you, you're too wild and free.
You represent a sense of danger which they don't wish to
   see
You capture creation in God's fullest glory
You travel along, each different place a different story.
You seek the sun like a bird in the winter
You talk like the greats, Shakespeare and Pinter.

The painter's dream of sun and creation
Turns to one of sudden realization
That his world is dark and cold
His paintings are ignored, his poems go untold.

Winter comes and the flowers they die
You mourn their passing, in your fields you cry,
Your eyes dim and your mouth wears a frown
Back from the country into the town.
Where reality's your biggest fear
There is no beauty to recreate here.
No birds in flight, no flowers in bloom
This place so cold and dark, our universal tomb.
Your dream ends as the dawn of reality breaks
See now, Painter, what your brush can create

The Painter's dream of sun and creation
Turns to one of sudden realization
That the world is dark and cold
His paintings are ignored, his poems go untold.

Caroline Villa (15)
St Mary's Secondary School,
Londonderry, N. Ireland

'Flowers of Glory' Lucy Barnard (11)
Moorfield Junior School, Bridlington, Humberside
(Highly commended)

Compact numbers

Module 2.1
Is ready for take-off;
Four hundred million
In each ship
Are up and away –
Four months in the sky!
The annual
Holiday begins.
Module 1.2
Is sinking to hell
For the time
Of freezing
In vaults of steel.
Too many are born;
Not enough
Pass on to heaven.
Module 3.1
On this mortal earth
Stays for the coughing,
The fighting and death.
Ten years
Is the waiting time
For birth
And the paper work
Will take
Three more.
Females decide at
Twelve or ten
And licences
Are issued then.
Doctors deliver
Two babies a minute;

Most are not as lucky as these
But, moving
On conveyor belts,
Granted life
By machine,
Are shipped to the end
Where the husband waits.
Not too romantic
To call
Your wife a number!

Steven Ralston (12)
Debenham High School,
Debenham,
Stowmarket, Suffolk

The destruction

When the grass began to die
The tests were quickly made.
One blood-shot eye squinted down a scientific cylinder
At a soil sample,
At millions upon millions of micro-beings.
'My God!' said the man in the white overall,
'We've just lost our countryside.'
Magnified on the slide in the electron microscope,
Masses of greenery were turning rapidly to bluish white,
Like mould on stale bread,
Unstoppable, plague-like.

Shane Ryan (13)
Ellen Wilkinson High School,
Manchester

Tree

'What's that?'
The little girl asked
As she sat in the machine.
'I think,' said the man,
'It is a tree,
A relic from
The time of flowers.'
The machine sped on,
Cutting its way
Through the artificial air
In the artificial town.
The tree was trapped,
For tourists' eyes,
In a plastic cage,
Among a mass
Of plastic towers,
Its branches bare;
Its leaves long dead.

Patricia Cope (13)
Debenham High School,
Debenham
Stowmarket, Suffolk

Fur, Feather, Fin...

Dinosaurs

There are no dinosaurs today.
So what? They'd eat us anyway!

Thomas Grieve (8)
Norwich, Norfolk
(Highly commended)

'The Rabbit'
Jenny Stewart (7)
Pitlochry, Perthshire

Slug

Shloup shlugal shlobsh shlip
Sligoosh skigoosh shligalop
Shiligigoloshlob skibablosh
Bleshoposlopsh

Puff! Pant! Nearly at the end of the cabbage leaf
Ah, time for another shlogoly bit of cabbage
Shlibylishious,
Oh no, here comes that stupid gardener again!
He must think I'm really stupid
If he thinks I'll eat those disgusting pellets,
Oh no, my sticky shlogy gunge isn't sticky enough
I'm falling,
It's alright I've landed in the long grass,
It'll take another week to get up on that leaf again
But I'm not in a hurry.

Jim Bremner (12)
Northmead County Middle School,
Guildford, Surrey

The Red Admiral

Her wings shimmer in the sun,
As she flies along in the wind, suddenly she
Is caught in a web.
WIGGLES,
But she can't get out of the web,
She falls asleep,
Forever.

Helen Thomas (7)
Stanley, Perthshire

Intermezzo

The piano sits alone,
huddled in the corner of the attic,
patiently waiting.
The lid is closed against inquisitive spiders,
busily spinning.
Until the silence is broken by a visitor,
quietly humming.

Long slender fingers caress the keys,
skilfully playing.
Vibrant music echoes around the room,
deeply enchanting.
Until the final crescendo dies away,
majestically ending.

The piano is once more alone,
patiently waiting.
The spiders resume their work,
confidently weaving.
Until music again fills them with joy,
everlasting.

Kirsty Pearce (11)
Newcastle-under-Lyme School,
Newcastle-under-Lyme, Staffs

Drone-death

Now is the time to remember dark mornings;
The dark and the mellow dusts,
The birth-holes, all full and slowly maturing,
And the hushed burr and the dance-steps.
We remember the summer's-plenty tastes;
Dimly recalled, of the deep gold.
And the dust caught in the head-hairs,
Floating between the waxes.

In this time we departed.
I myself was one of the many;
I remember the dizzy explosion of blue,
The cool, the noise and the flight;
We, the many, to follow the One.
I was not the first and did not end,
Not then, in the unfelt ecstasy.

We, the many, returned to the dust,
The waxes, the grubs and the birth-holes.
As the summer ebbed we waited,
Not moving much, just to use the dark gatherings,
Food in the dimness, remembering.

Now the gold is scarcer.
We are to die in the dazzling blue.
As the One and the rest must continue.
Perhaps soon we must leave the mellow dark.
It is now that the time has come to remember dark
    mornings.

Louise Bagshawe (17)
Woldingham School,
Nr Caterham, Surrey
(Italian Tour Award winner)

Aboot a moose

A frichtsome wee beastie
Rattles awa' at the flairbuirds
A paw gets through
Noo an airm an' hauf his heid
The rest o' his body shin follies
But süne he's awa doon the hole
Wi' a biscuit or cake or cheese
Or onythin' else he kin lay his haun's on
He disnae ken the fuss he's caused
The weemin he's scairt

Yin nicht he comes up frae his hole
Sniffin an' scurryin' aboot
Searchin' fir vittals
Syne he sniffs oot cheese
He attacks it
Like it's alive
A metal bar flees up an ower his body
But catches his heid an smashes his skull
There'll be nae mair scratchin' in the nicht
Nae scrams in the day

A nice quiet hoose
Nae mair moose!

Adele Barrowman (14)
West Calder High School, Limefield,
Polbeth, West Lothian
(Highly commended)

Danger for the rockpool

A black layer of oil threatens the creatures.
Limpets and mussels close tightly,
The happy creatures of the rockpool
Are near their peril.
The oil looms nearer,
Killing every sea creature in its path.
The once clear sea is nearly history.
Oil covers the rocks.
Hundreds of hermit crabs die,
Mussels, clams and limpets suffocate.
The tide goes
But the oil stays in the rockpool.
Useless is oxygen
With oil to block it out
The last of the limpets graze
On the left seaweed.
A year later the rockpool
Is nearly back to normal
But never the same as before.

Glenn Everett (7)
St Cedd's School, Chelmsford,
Essex

Fishing

little boy walking past a pond
about the age of three
watching the fish
weaving and winding in and out of lilies
dips a net in the water
catches a fish
the water drips and dribbles
out of the net
the fish dries up and crinkles
the boy doesn't know
what's happened
his mother comes out to find him
she shouts at him
'come in don't stay out all night'
the little boy drops the net
it splashes in the water

Jill Leigh (11)
Whalley CE Primary School, Whalley,
Blackburn, Lancs

Quo cibo vescitur?

And then we saw the Heron
standing on one
slender, glistening leg.
Concentration.
Eyes rooted
on the river's undulating membrane.
Spear at the ready.
Now!
You missed it. Only to see
the scales catch the sun
and to imagine
the bulge running down
the long,
painted neck.

A spring!
He is articulating
symmetrically.
Now an image . . .

Back to the foxgloves,
the sparrows,
the murmurs of the pub.
They have their beer,
their pasties.
The pure efficiency
of the exchange
makes that important . . .
but where's the risk?

Claire Davis (13)
Newcastle-under-Lyme School,
Newcastle-under-Lyme, Staffs
(Highly commended –
Arthur Lines Poetry Award winner)

Feeding the birds

In the garden silent and
still everything is peaceful.
Suddenly noise, children laughing.
Putting food out for the birds.
The birds are timid they are
frightened.
Suddenly out come the birds
looking, bobbing heads, all sizes,
eyes peeping.
Birds swooping
Greedily eat all the food.
Blue tits
Clever tricks, swinging on the nuts
Like acrobats balancing.
Water splashing everywhere.
Tails wagging, very fat birds,
Tired birds flying off slowly.

Caroline Smallwood (6)
Marston Green Infant School,
Marston Green, Birmingham

The toad

He crouched
Stone-still,
Like a small speckled rock;
With pulsating throat,
He looked so helpless,
So terrified.

His strong legs
Were folded,
Like springs,
Held close.

Light as a leaf,
As big as my palm,
He sat in the scoop
Of my hands.

Now, his pads,
Like minute claws,
Cling for life.
His tiny toes
Clutch my fingertips.

His skin is lumpy,
Soft and bumpy,
His rough belly
Warming my palm.

So eager, so anxious
To run from me,
He does not know
I am harmless;
He is beautiful.
If only he knew!

Helen Southwood (13)
Debenham High School,
Debenham,
Stowmarket, Suffolk

'Heron and Herring'
Jane Barrie (14)
Uddingston, Glasgow

The fox and the crow

an old proverb in rhyme with a somewhat irregular ending

A crow sat up top in the boughs of a tree,
Clutching some cheese that he'd stolen for tea,
But this wasn't the cheese that just any crow wangles –
The devious bird had pinched Kraft sliced cheese singles.

Whilst removing the wrappings from his ill-gotten prize,
A sly fox came up and, with starved, hungry eyes,
Began to think how he best could cajole
The crow into parting with what he had stole.

At first he began with a heart-felt plea,
Saying, 'Crow, do you know what that cheese means to
      me?
For I've not taken food in over a week
And would relish most dearly that cheese in your beak.'

But the crow, I'm afraid, felt no sympathy
Since he thought that Fox looked as well-fed as could be,
So he carried on chomping, no cares in the world,
While the fox paced around, and pondered, and growled.

He then spoke in rather less courteous tones,
Saying, 'Give me that cheese or I'll break all your bones.'
But Crow knew that Fox couldn't climb the tall tree
And thought to himself, 'Ha! You won't get me!'

Now Crow had the last piece of cheese in his beak,
And while holding this was unable to speak,
So Fox, with a plan which he thought could not fail,
Looked up at the crow, swishing his tail.

'Oh, Crow,' he said fawningly, laying it on thick,
'It's obvious I won't fool you with a trick,
But before you depart, just to help me along,
Could you possibly sing me your wonderful song?'

Now it's true crows aren't famed for their musical ways,
But, just like us, are most flattered by praise,
And this one, he ALMOST burst into song,
But suddenly realized what could go wrong.

For he still had that large piece of cheese in his chops –
If he'd started to sing, it would fall to the fox.
Having spotted this ploy he glowed warmly with pride,
While the fox down below rolled over and cried.

But as he crawled silently, slowly away,
Fox jumped with joy when he heard the crow say,
In a moment of foolishness, being rather thick,
'So you thought I would fall for that silly old tr . . .'

! !

Euan Lees (15)
Hutchesons Grammar School, Glasgow

Eternal rhythm

The spluttering and coughing
Of an old engine
Shuddering
Across a motionless field
Scatters
Birds on an empty sky.

The evil machine
Churns and crushes
Damp sods
As sharp blades,
Glinting in the sunlight,
Slice
Through the earth,
Scraping
And scattering stones
Leaving
In its wake a dark scar
Oozing
Slippery worms
Exposed to the
Scavenging gulls.

Sam Dalziel (13)
All Saints Middle School,
Sudbury, Suffolk

Snake and mouse

I watch you without emotion.
You, eyes bright in the tall wet grass,
You snuffle at the ground,
Whiskers aquiver.
I wait for my moment.
You sit up and sniff the air,
Warm and tender, hesitantly alert.
I am motionless; I am dangerous.

In one eternal second I uncoil.
You are paralysed, helpless
And my potential is unleashed.
You are frozen
And ripples of power surge through my anguine body.
Time stands still
And I flick between the green blades.
A whip lashing out,
I dart at you and my jaws snap shut
Around your vulnerable body.
Spell broken, you squeal and writhe.
I wait,
Immobile
For you to die.

Rowena Hazell (14)
Debenham High School, Debenham,
Stowmarket, Suffolk

Python

I'm a Python
Thick as a sapling's trunk
I eat pig
Raw Pig
Live Pig
Head first
The stumpy snout in my throat
And jelly eyeballs against the roof of my mouth
My jaw stretches open
And my ribs widen.
As I swallow this pig
The pig's back legs kick pushing him further in
All of a sudden
He's motionless.
Slides down like butter.

Mark Appleton (11)
Northmead County Middle School,
Guildford, Surrey
(Highly commended)

Hunter

When the moon is full
And the sky is dark
With dots of silvered clouds,
A cat,
With charcoal coat
And fire-gold eyes,
Talons extended ready,
Will leap
From the midnight air.

Like child-drawn daisies
His footprints remain
As he stalks among frosted leaves;
A cat,
With light-shattered coat
Bristled like spines
And teeth gleaming ready,
Will leap
From the midnight air.

Crouched in a menacing light
Against the sombre skies,
With a chant of death,
A cat,
With muscles taut
And body poised,
Eyes so ruthless and cold,
Will kill
In the midnight air.

Rachael Pearson (11)
Debenham High School, Debenham,
Stowmarket, Suffolk

In the dead of night

The sleek, black cat slinks
In the dead of night,
Her tail twitching.
With the bright quarter moon reflected in her glossy coat
She carefully balances across the crumbling wall
Down on to the cobbled street.
She cautions at a broken bottle,
Then carries on round the dustbins,
Down an alleyway, where she hears the sorrowful
   whimper
Of a dog, chained to a tree.
But the cat does not take pity on the moaning bundle,
She just walks on,
Her soft paws gently touching the mossy steps.
She squeezes through the patterned gate,
Up a step and through the flap,
To the safe grasp of her master's arms.

Katherine Gagie (11)
Higham, Nr Rochester, Kent

'The Pups'
Lucy Campbell (11)
Kilgraston School,
Bridge of Earn,
Perthshire
(Highly commended)

Muffin – my dog

Muffin the mongrel
Has long, droopy ears,
A fringe that covers his eyes,
And a tail like a fan.
He has eyes that shine
In the night.
When I come downstairs
They sparkle – greeny black
Like cat eyes.
He has bits of hair
That stick up – spiky
Like a punk rocker's.
When he opens his mouth,
His tongue hangs out
Between his teeth.
He looks like
He is laughing.

Hayley Morris (7)
St Brigid's RC J & I School,
Northfield, Birmingham

Our visit to the zoo

*(by 3A4, who 'borrowed' the first verse and invented the
others)*

We went to the Zoo
We saw a gnu
An elk and a whelk
And a wild kangaroo.

We saw a giraffe
Whose neck made us laugh,
And a whale flip his tail
Whilst taking a bath.

We saw a seal
Who was eating his meal,
Of a fish from a dish,
With a joyful squeal.

We saw a bear
Covered in fur,
And a skunk that stunk
But didn't care.

We saw a cockatoo
Creating a to-do,
We saw an ape eat a grape
And a big banana too.

We saw a white rabbit
That had a bad habit,
His nose twitched and snitched,
As a boy tried to grab it.

We saw a snake
That was hardly awake
And a lion eat meat
They'd forgotten to bake.

We saw a zoo keeper
Attacked by a cheetah,
And a mouse in its house
Keeping warm by a heater.

At the end of the day
We wanted to stay
But 'Sir' didn't care
And he drove us away.

Group Work (13)
Rainford High School,
Rainford, St Helens, Merseyside

'Swan Song'
Camilla Wesson (13)
High Wycombe, Bucks

My pony

Released into her field,
She flings herself into an enormous buck,
Her hooves like gold cymbals
As the sun glints on them.
Then with grunts of delight,
She lowers herself to the ground.
She squirms, snorting in ecstasy,
As every itch is removed.
Refreshed, she jumps nimbly to her feet.
She circles the field at a floating canter,
Her neck stretched out and tail kinked over her back,
As she sniffs the wind.
Her head held high, nose lifted,
Searching the air.
Then, after a last wild whinny,
She settles down contentedly to graze.

Victoria Fry (11)
St Mary's School,
Ascot, Berkshire

Other languages

all the whales telling all the
others to go to another country
before all the ice comes and they
will be trapped.
all the cats and kittens calling
each other for dinner before it's all
gone.

and all the sheep shouting when it's
tea time.
all the cows shouting when they have
babies.
all the seals going honk honk because
of the virus going around the sea.
all the owls hooting in the night
telling the owls to get up.
people use hand language to tell
people things.
dogs bark for help and when people
are in trouble.
guide dogs help people walk down
steps and cross roads that's how dogs
give language.
dark makes language to the light so
someone turns it on.
people just move their mouths for
language.
you can draw for Language.
you can think without Language.
the earth Tells the trees to lose
their leaves.
horses shout when someone tries to
catch them.

Gemma Atkins (7)
Mousehold Avenue First School,
Norwich, Norfolk
(Highly commended)

Times and Seasons

Days of the week

Monday is: going for a run day
having lots of fun day
sitting in the sun day
eating a sticky bun day

Tuesday is: buying new shoes day
looking for clues day
watching the news day
playing in the loos day

Wednesday is: making new friends day
an it depends day
clucking hens day
felt-tipped pens day

Thursday is: learning new words day
stroking soft furs day
feeding the birds day
pussy-cat purrs day

Friday is: eating strawberry pie day
getting the washing dry day
saying goodbye day
wearing a pretty tie day

Saturday is: it doesn't matter day
time for a chatter day
rain, pitter-patter, day
toys clutter clatter day

Sunday is: getting things done day

Group Work (5/6)
Nunnery Wood Primary School,
Worcester
(Highly commended)

'That Monday Feeling'
Cathryn Keeler (17)
Maidstone Grammar School
for Girls, Maidstone, Kent
(Italian Tour Award winner)

137

Sundial

Granite face embraced by lichen.
Mossed, softly embossed with Roman runes:
a sturdy stone
stands here alone
and here has stood for many centuries of noons.

Shadows trace the moving sun.
I finger-trace the weathered lines:
a fine invention,
only to function
when the soothing sunlight shines.

Without emotion, it marks the lives
of hours which come to be, then perish:
they make a day,
then pass away
as moments only memory will cherish.

Rebecca Torrens (17)
Newcastle-under-Lyme School,
Newcastle-under-Lyme, Staffs

Spring

When I see the yellow aconites,
Hear the thrushes sing,
Touch the furry catkins,
I know it must be spring.

Kate Moss (10)
Hexham, Northumberland

Rain

Down the window pane
Dribble drops of rain.
I stop them with my finger
But they always start again.

Joanna Knight (7)
Kent College Junior School,
Tunbridge Wells, Kent

Sun

Glittering, shining shocking sun
Light sun, hot sun
You were there yesterday
Why aren't you
there today?
Across the sky you move
your pale yellow across the blue sky
You shine through bare trees
like a torch shining through sticks
Those nine planets orbit you
You great round sun
You travel slowly across the sky.

Gemma Perry (7)
R A Butler Junior School,
Saffron Walden, Essex

Paper sun

Paper sun,
It's out today;
But when the paper
Burns away,
Night time
Comes to stay.

Rachael Smith (4)
Leigh-on-Sea, Essex

'Year of the Dragon' Christine Pollin (17)
Hereford School, Grimsby, South Humberside

Poppy

A shout,
Like a machine gun, rattles
Across a barren waste
Where nothing moves
And spiders spin
Gigantic webs
Of sprawling steel
That twist and tangle,
Tear and rip
The ragged wind.
And on that wind
Floats a solitary grain
Of amber and grey,
Spiralling down
To be consumed
By lakes of rust.
It sleeps in the sludge
And lies, like a mine,
Waiting for a touch.
With a burst, it explodes,
Throwing tongues of flame
That do not burn.
And, when they die,
They leave behind
More seeds to bloom
For all mankind.

Tony Roberts (13)
Debenham High School,
Debenham,
Stowmarket, Suffolk

The midsummer symphony

The sun took out his conducting rod,
   One, two, three!
The cuckoo-pint saw he was on,
   And boomed a big bass 'C'
Rose of Sharon unfurled her petals
   And joined with alto lilt,
While meadowsweet's one thousand flowers
   A tinkling soprano built.
And through it all the cuckoo-pint
   Boomed his big bass 'C'
Then who should join with a bold, bright 'G'
   Than trumpeting peony?
All at once the musicians were quiet,
   A chord hung in the sky;
And all were still for sweet-pea's bill,
   A gentle lullaby.
Three bars later columbine joined
   Sweet-pea's soft, calm medley
And matched the tune to perfection,
But in a slightly lower key.
Water lily's light baritone
   Joined in the little phrase
And with primrose formed a quartet
For a quiet, little phase.
Boom ba-boom! Boom! Boom!
   The trumpet proclaimed so loud
And bindweed broke the spell of slumber
   In brassy, clear note sound.
Then daffodil lifted her beautiful face
   To form a clear alto
While poppy shouted at joyful top
   Telling all she was soprano!

Then tulip struck a strident note
  All other sounds were shushed
And lily of the valley played a tentative tune
  As her audience became quite hushed.
Now little snowdrop joined the lilt
  With bluebell and daisy too
And buttercup played a friendly 'E'
  Together with forget-me-not blue.
Up, up trilled scarlet pimpernel,
  Who was given the highest part;
Her little red body strained so hard,
  As she sang with all her heart.
Pansy struck a mischievous 'F sharp'
  (Which was her favourite art)!
Narcissus began a rollicking tune,
  And Iris followed soon
As dandelion struck the beat of a march
  To start the final tune.
The orchestra played both high and low –
  With heart – for days on end
And swinging to the last impressive chord,
  The finale came to an end.

Lisa Wilson (11)
Northwick, Worcester

Summer

In the trees there's rustling leaves
And when the sun is shining
then I went to the sea.
And a little baby was crying
the waves were whispering
the seagulls were tossing
in the sky.
And I'm just watching.

Ruth Lings (7)
Rushcombe First School,
Corfe Mullen, Wimborne, Dorset

Playing with words

Sea is cold and splashy,
Splashy as my sister in the bath,
Bath before I go to bed,
Bed is warm and snuggly,
Snuggly as some teddy bears.
Teddy bears are fluffy,
Fluffy are the snowflakes,
Snowflakes melt into water,
Water, in the lakes.
Lakes where surfboarders surf,
Surfboarders surf in the rolling waves,
Waves, in the sea.

Emma Slack (7)
St Cedd's School, Chelmsford,
Essex

'Garden Centre' Alexander Richardson (7)
Tavistock & Summerhill School, Haywards Heath, West Sussex

Autumn

The leaves are falling
off the trees
In Autumn before
the freeze

Michelle Hoskin (5)
Garras CP School,
Mangan,
Helston, Cornwall

Silent night fever

October,
yes, Your Royal Hypeness,
the push has begun.
Load up your bags with some festive filled fun.
Santa
Claus bared.
Kids hooked
and snared.
Urge to buy, to have, to hold.
'Sorry Sir, good cheer was sold.'
M & S 'Penny Bazaar',
trouble is they never are.
Oh, the spirit of the occasion:
mainly Martini in my estimation.
But the press aren't
out of the gutter.
Headline news of the
Queen's pre-speech stutter.
Now follow the weeks
of special programmes.
Minds to the slaughter
like biblical lambs.
Material gain of presents galore.
Girls' plastic dolls and boys' plastic war.
Silent night fever,
the time bomb's in store.

Alison Pember (16)
The Grove School, St Leonards on Sea,
East Sussex
(Highly commended)

A silver sea

I look out my window
and see a silver sea,
it spreads over moorland,
hedge and tree,
over land and over sea.
In through the window
and rests on me.

Claire Ruell (11)
Leintwardine School,
Craven Arms, Shropshire

'Boat Builders' Lupin Rahman (13)
Nonsuch High School for Girls, Cheam, Surrey

The marsh mist

after reading Chapter 1 of Great Expectations

Shrouded in marsh mist
mildewed tombs lift weary heads
above the damp yellow-grey wreaths.
Fingering, lingering,
whispering to the dead.

Melancholy marsh mist
seeping, creeping between sodden laths.
Dank hulks shudder beneath
their burden of human misery.
Mist,
fingering, lingering,
hissing to those who might as well be dead.

Morbid, the marsh mist
probes the starkness of the gibbet,
sniffs the air of execution
and carries it this way, that way,
souring the flat fenlands.
Fingering, lingering,
crooning to the dead.

Neil Mathieson (10)
Treliske School, Highertown,
Truro, Cornwall

Winter

When I go out
To play
And it's snowy
And misty,
Immediately the wind
Bites me.
The mist
Swallows everything up
In its huge mouth.
People run in and out
Of the gaping mouth –
But when I try,
The mouth seems
To keep going backwards
So I can never
Get into it.

Timothy Hall (10)
Bushey Middle School,
Raynes Park, London

Seven snowmen

We built seven
Snowmen my
brother and me.
Some of them
had no heads.
Some of them
were fat. Some
of them had
faces, and
some didn't.
All of them
Were different,
But one thing
They were all
Cold. And so
Were we!
My brother
and me.

Vanessa Steele (5)
White Hills
Lower School,
Northampton
(Highly
commended)

A snowy day

The frozen footsteps of the chapped-faced boy
Shivering through the moonlight
The six-sided star drifted to the ground and melted
Under the grey clouds he saw a starving robin
It flutters to the ground
Its glowing chest gently fading
Heart breaking, worrying
He wrapped the shivering breast in a scarf of fine
And laid the gallant bird down.
And watched as its breast goes out,
He retrieves his muffler and catches the flakes
Which melt on his numb hand.

Giles Scott (9)
Spittal VC School, Spittal,
Haverfordwest, Pembrokeshire

'The Eagle' Jonathan Goldsmith (7) Lincewood Junior School,
Langdon Hill, Basildon, Essex

Glesga

Noo tha' i's colt in ol' Glesga toon,
Wains star' tae greet an' get' bored pre'y soon,
Trains an' buses 'come mare an' mare terdy,
An' 'Dinkies' scoot passed with their swankey cers,
Ready fur wurk a' tall office blocks,
Wheel the Festival ge's pu' doon, a're a' the docks,
Un'er the Umbrella drunks lie in the stree's,
Then tae Cen'ral where 'wan' mee's.

A're a' 'Princes Squer', the 'trendies' gather,
Up tae the tope tae hev a wee blether,
Doon tae Merks tae buy year sokes,
Ye even pie fur the flippin' pokes,
Roun' the pubs, ar' busy wi' cha'er,
An' wipets si' ootside in the gu'er
Aye, i's colt doon 'ere in Glesga,
But i's ma hame, forever.

Gillian Wright (13)
Westbourne School for Girls, Glasgow

Waiting for winter

January is now a missing person.
His description is well . . .
well . . . I suppose
WHITE.
He is dressed in a white suit and hat
and like the Sun he has got it on.
His smile is dazzling white.
Police are anxious to trace him
as he's wanted by many disappointed children.
Has he been kidnapped?
If so Police will be looking
for a gang with frozen fingers.
Is he suffering from amnesia?
Has he flaked out somewhere?
A reward is offered for information
leading to the arrest of January Snow.
Meanwhile a substitute will be taking his place.
She is called April.
This explains the mild weather
which is set to continue
for quite a while.

Julia Wearn (10)
Cloudside County Junior School,
Sandiacre, Nottingham
(Highly commended)

Things Mysterious

O moon O moon

O moon O moon I wish you were so low
Then I could stroke you.
Then we could go to the park and play.
You could fly and I could walk.
We could meet my friends who live in a hole: Mummy
    Bear, Daddy Bear, Baby Bear.
Then you could show me all your friends.
We could stay up all night.
You could make the light,
Because you are a moon.

Anna Karlin (4)
London
(Highly commended)

Never put the moon in a tin

I tried.
I saw it glistening
In the sky.
I climbed up high to get it down.
I put it on the ground to have a proper look.
It was shivering.
I wrapped it up in a woolly scarf.
Its silver surface glistened.
I took it home and put it in a tin.
Then I went to bed.
Suddenly I woke up.
I heard a noise,
The rattling of a tin.
I took out the moon.
Its silver surface had turned to grey.
The glisten had completely gone.
I turned around and looked outside.
Everything was dark.

Samantha Kerr (11)
Whalley CE Primary School,
Whalley, Blackburn, Lancs

Time for bed

Put awa' your book
Turn off the light
Day is düne
Night has begun

Let me tuck you in
All snug and tight
Dream awa' my bairn
Night's just begun

It's a' dark ootside
There's nae stern light
Everyone's quiet
Noo night's begun

I close tight my een
Hide under my covers
Feart to mak' a sound
Syne night's begun

That frichtsome monster
Under ma bed
Is haein' a braw time
Now night's begun

There's mair than one
O' them eldritch sights
Hauntin' ma room
Syne night's begun

They're ahint my curtains
Dancin' on my wa's
Oot they a' come
Now night's begun

I pray to God
Ilka night
To send them awa'
When night's begun

But they willnae go
Wi'oot a fight
So ah'll just hae to wait
Til' morning light

Donna Drever (14)
West Calder High School,
Limefield, Polbeth,
West Lothian

Spell to tidy my bedroom

Put a piece of carpet in
A few bits of fluff and dirt
An eye of a teddy bear
My doll's hand and foot in.
Mix it well with some carpet
Don't forget to mix it well.
A little bit of shelf
A lot of wall paper
Doesn't matter what kind
Pink, blue or even yellow
Who would care about the colour
Make it boil and bubble well
Still stir it very well
Use the other end of the carpet
A picture frame from a picture
A picture that is on the wall
Mix it in as well
A peace of bed quilt
A pencil that you use
To do your homework with
When you have mixed it
Watch it work
Go out the room for ten minutes.
When you come back in
You will see it has worked.

Victoria Chaplain (8)
Glenmead JI School,
Great Barr, Birmingham

What's that down there?

What's that down there?
What's that moving?
What's that moving down
in the dark?
Is it the monster
Who roars
And kills?
Or is it the skeleton
Who rattles his bones?
What's that down there?
What's that moving?
What's that moving down
in the dark?
Is it a bat
Flying through the air?
What's that
in the dark?

Jonathan Matthews (7)
St George's County Junior
School, Copthorne,
Shrewsbury

Night fears

When I come home from school
I hang up my coat on the door;
The side facing into my bedroom.

I've got a mask; a big green mask,
Hanging from my bedpost,
Just where I can see it in the mirror.

In the middle of the night
The clock strikes twelve.
I wake up with a start.

Hey, wait a minute!
My coat is moving;
First one sleeve, then the other.

There is a rustling by my bedpost:
I can see in the mirror my mask is moving,
Jerking up and down to try and get free.

Behind the eyes a light is shining;
Like a fire,
Getting always brighter.

A wind comes through the crack in the doorway,
Low and subtle,
Whispering fear.

A force is pushing me out of my bed.
I am slowing rolling over the edge;
My throat tightens, and I am falling . . . falling . . .

Rebecca Daker (10)
London

The ghost

I am the light of the candle
I draw air from the breath of a newly born robin.
I am like the yellow, burnt page of a Bible
   I am like the hands of a globe,
I steer myself towards the end of eternity
I move like the waves of dried grass drawn
   Up in a howl of wind.

Angela Macdonald (11)
Prestonfield Primary School, Edinburgh

The good dragon

Come for a ride he calls.
Climb upon my back.
Mind my spines
They prick.
Hold tight
It's going to be bumpy.
Bring some water and a tea bag
And a slice of bread.
My flaming breath
will boil the water
We will have toast and tea.

Emma Harkness (8)
St John's CE School,
Dukinfield, Tameside

The Preston witch

There was an old witch from Preston,
Who asked herself this question,
Was it the rats,
The snails or the bats,
That gave her acute indigestion?

Sara Jones (9)
Clifton County Primary School,
St Annes-on-Sea, Lancs

The Rainbow Serpent

The Earth was flat.
Nothing stirred, no sound at all.

Far beneath the earth,
The Rainbow Serpent,
The Mother of Life,
Was uncurling from her cramped sleep.

She started up the tunnel,
A boulder stopped her in her tracks.

Her big belly was full,
With all earth's creatures,
She pushed and pushed until,
Suddenly, it burst open.
'My first new birth I shall call
Uluru!'

She wandered the Earth,
Making hollows by slithering,
Making holes where she slept.

She felt the creatures inside her,
They were impatient,
She slid back to her first born,
Slowly,
The frog tribe came out,
With much water in their stomachs,
After the long hibernation inside her.

She tickled them,
The water flowed out,
Making streams, rivers, seas and oceans,
In the hollows she made on her
Travels.

The creatures that broke her laws,
She turned to stone,
Making the rocks and mountains,
Those that obeyed her laws,
Became human.

Rachel Simmons (11)
Paulton Junior School,
Paulton, Nr Bristol, Avon

The ammonite

A doorway to the past,
A mystery
A tale of things gone by.
A spiral staircase,
A way to travel back through time.
A black hole of darkness,
A missing link.
It is the eye of the past.
It knows all,
But tells nothing.
A key to the future,
A key to the past.
It has slipped the net of time.

James Hallett (11)
Pentlepoir CP School, Pentlepoir,
Saundersfoot, Dyfed

Translation of a piece of paper

A piece of paper,
Frost-ribbed platforms
Channelled in ink-sprayed mats,
Ink growing and Escalating!
Shrinking and Constricting!
Ascending and Descending!
Into slanting . . . parachuting words,
From an unseen document,
Misused words
From an indefinite tongue,
Flanking words
From letters A to Z.

And behind these flanking words
Are other words,
Independent of capital letters
And full stops,
Positioned
Like pieces in a Game of Chess –

Within these other words
And through different, unnoticed doors,
I search
The rugged and jagged mountains
Of such sentences and words,
Finding a new language
More human and alien than the last,
A language
Hidden within the written language,
Lost before discovered,
Found before known.

And within such a language,
There are many stars
Traced upon forged words,
There are many stars
Glowing as saffron, scattered seeds
Among sage-swept steppes,
And perhaps
There is also
The coral-fluted sun,
Scattered
As an army in flames
Would scatter itself upon the horizon –
The blindfolded princess
Who has not yet matured.

And lost . . . entangled . . . ensnared . . .
In this line-propelling jungle
Of unapproached words,
There is also
The fiction of the future,
The unevaded facts of the present,
And finally
The unrealized legends of the past.

On the other side
Of this unobstructed page
Is the auburn-sweating margin,
And finally
There is the ashen-fading moonlight,
Of an unobstructed war,
Where
My eyes are my enemies
And my gun is my uncertain friend.

And next to letter 'T'
Is the inerrant private
Throwing back
The Germans
To the starting line.

And here at the end
Of the tune,
The pianist will play
Liszt's *Second Piano Concerto* again,
Enscribed as three letters:
Letter 'E'
Letter 'O'
Letter eternity!

Steven Mercer (12)
Orpington, Kent

'*A Lonely Cottage*' *Glenna Williams (13)*
Sir Hugh Owen Lower School, Caernarfon, Gwynedd

The birth

As they enter the stable
There is an immediate pungency.
The dim light
Shows a rotting wooden trough
Their audience
Unperturbed by their presence.
They wait.
They long for warmth and love.
In their weariness they lie
On the sharp hay
Waiting for a miracle
In the darkness of the stable.

Syrena Mitchell (10)
St Mary's RC School,
Gillingham, Kent

On the Move

Bus pandemonium – homeward bound

Little Jack Horner sits in a corner
reading a concert programme.
Whilst Little Bo Peep has lost her money
(all over the floor)
Sir has found a magic pipe
and Genie is sprawling all over the chair.
Humpty Dumpty has fallen off his seat.
Left behind are the two babes who are lost
in the wood of people.
Jack is starting to climb the mountain
of litter
and it's not just the beans that are talking.
Teacher shouts 'You're behaving like nursery children.
This trip has been a real pantomime.'

Katherine Smith (10)
Cloudside County Junior School,
Sandiacre, Nottingham

Board in' the bus

I wandered lonely in the bus,
My skirt felt much too tight.
I knew 'Brown Owl' would make a fuss;
She'd never see the light.

My red mohican, ram rod stiff;
Scintillating brightly;
Contrasted with her mousy quiff.
She really looked unsightly!

Creamy collar, Nottingham lace,
Anaemic face, veined blue.
Her 'Jaegar' outfit worn with grace;
A subtle blending hue.

My chains and bracelets jangled loud,
Thick make-up dark and strong.
Black leathers stood out in the crowd;
Gild studded, shining, thonged.

Along the back graffitied seat;
Supine, I clacked my gum,
Rhythmically I beat my feet
Like a heavy metal drum.

I craved for 'Meatloaf' and boyfriend Daz,
But Brown Owl had a tape
Of Ging gang goolie goolie guide songs;
Our minds with which to shape.

Pensively I stretched my gum,
Then fixed it to the seat.
The hours ahead could well be glum.
Must I endure this treat?

I thought of Daz the Bomber,
I yearned to do a turn;
And wondered whether Brown Owl
Would like to try *my* fun!!!

Tanya Simpson (16)
Stanton-by-Dale, Ilkeston,
Derbyshire

'The Betting Office' Craig Maynard (14)
Merrywood Boys School, Knowle, Bristol, Avon

Trivialities

Why do more buses always go past,
On the other side of the road?
Why do people always manage to arrive a minute before
The bus you've been waiting hours for?
Why does nobody tell you it's one of the main functions
   in life?
Eating, drinking, sleeping, going on the loo, and waiting
   for buses.
Mozart probably could have written another concerto,
If he didn't have to keep waiting for the number twelve.
Scot would have probably been the first to the Pole,
If his bus hadn't got held up in snow-storms:
Why is it that the buses have to go on strike,
And leave you stranded in the middle of nowhere,
When you have an exam you've actually revised for?
What's the use of a philosophical thirteen year old girl
Who just can't accept
The trivialities of life?

Jade Widocks (13)
Bolton School Girls Division, Bolton
(Highly commended)

Agnus Dei in the car

Beatus Vir serenades a
half-moon,
suspended in a resonating horizon,
tenors and baritones saunter
down the motorway,
past Sirius and A521 exit,
Laudate Dominum and those
salient-like yellow lights
press up against the window,
reflecting a smooth and slightly suave posture
and the professor himself
coolly overtakes rival Renaults,
countryside sound asleep.
Clouds which once hated us
sweetly project
Chanson du Chévrier,
middle-aged bridges slink away
into the distance and
the services, 3, 2, 1, gone forever.

Simon Wales (16)
Lichfield, Staffs

Driving down a steep hill at night

A hill leading down to a valley.
Head lamps light up the floating reservoir.
The moon from the back lightens the way
And slowly moving down the hill
Things in a flickering quiet do not fit.

Cattle in corners: dull stumps.
Chains slack, heads rise, praying to the great.
Fields burn, move in lulls and shift.
The blue movement of tightness greets
The water which lies in a stamping of light.

The hill is pulled up from behind.
Flat land. Everything is gentle.
But until tomorrow things are held,
For night is enough and
Has not been slowed by the habits of day.

Alice Allen (17)
St Lawrence, Jersey

MBE to RIP

Percy Snodgrass MBE (later to be RIP),
Went to Auntie Maud for tea,
With ears pinned back and hair slicked down,
He left for Bognor Regis town.

He crouched down low behind the wheel,
A man of iron, a man of steel.
He revved to 90 miles an hour,
His foot went down, he felt the power.

Suddenly a cough and splutter,
The gearbox 'floated' to the gutter.
The doors both fell upon the ground.
But from our Percy came no sound.

Now he lies in holy ground,
And elsewhere in a tiny mound
There rests of car no trace nor odour,
Just nuts and bolts from tortured Skoda.

Rowan Urry (14)
St Edwards School, Charlton Kings,
Cheltenham, Glos

The road home

The jutting, jagged iron roofs,
Cut like razors through the air.
They oppress his twinkling mind
As he flicks back his hair.

He taps his fingers awkwardly
On the dashboard of his car
The rhythms jangle nervously
And tease a vertebra.

Industrial machinery
Lurks behind those silent walls
That pushed and pumped untiringly
Within those darkened halls.

The car swishes onwards,
He's trying to escape,
The dying debris of our time,
He fears he is too late.

The darkness is incisive,
Sharpened into night.
He dodges through the heavy shadows,
And passes into light.

The factories retreating,
Their walls stunned and fatigued,
Too tired to accept gaudy paint,
Too old to be intrigued.

The factories reflect his face,
A remnant of the past
A lived-in, dirty relic, allowed
To collapse at last.

Chris Saunders (15)
Burnham Grammar School,
Burnham, Nr Slough

'*A Restful Place*' *Clair Tregenza (17)*
Penwith Sixth Form College, Penzance, Cornwall

Moving north with a daughter

You will not remember the thickness of trees
Or the quiet roads on our crowd of hills;
Sussex swelling her rivers and blowing cold.

Yorkshire slopes gentle and plunges deep;
It is all one to you on the garden rug,
The kiss of heather here, and the great spaces.

I remember villages spoiling for ground,
Rocks in the primal floor of the wood;
And I hear the small wicked sounds of your chuckle
Bubbling up, and bursting like bubbles.

Louise Bagshawe (17)
Woldingham School, Nr Caterham,
Surrey
(Italian Tour Award winner)

Cadbury's night out

As I Buttoned up my overcoat,

A Whisper blew through the trees,
I caught a Double Decker up to Quality Street,
But Caramel wasn't there.
My mind was in a Twirl
What now I wondered?

I sat in the Lion bar
Then went on along to Rose's,
And as I strode into the Crunchie snow
I felt like Flaking out.
I needed a Boost
Life is no Picnic.

Aranda Bateson (13)
Dudley, Cramlington, Northumberland

In a hot-air-balloon

Into banks of sun
above the drifts,
of quilted clouds.
Rising and turning
without a sound
as Summer lifts us
off the ground.
Still as a bird
transfixed in flight.

Donella Dee-Cutler (10)
Eldene Junior School,
Colingsmead,
Eldene, Swindon,
Wilts

Flying finish

His hand twitched.
My knees squeezed.
Wham!
Automatic doors open.
Kick. Off.
Mud flying. Must keep my wits about me.
Squeeze.
Round the corner.
Squeeze, kick.
What if I forget my orders?
My life passes in front of my eyes.
Punter's money, watching crowd, prospective owner,
    expecting trainer.
Final furlong.
Kick, squeeze, thrust, push.
Hands go forward and back in a rhythm.
Rumbling crowds getting louder and louder.
Brightly coloured shapes all around.
I can't get through. Split second. Daylight.
Go! Kick, kick.
Red pole in sight.
Green on right. Yellow on left.
I am closing.
Time is running out.
Push harder. Go! Go!
Kick. Squeeze.
Made it!
Phew, just in time.
Slow down, turn around. Canter back.
Smiling faces greet us.

Dorothy-Ann Gerrard (15)
Edinburgh

Space Olympics?

Pluto won
long jump today
from the sun
Mercury got
gold
in running
Earth got
bronze
Mars
went red
after
coming fourth
Saturn
tried to
run
rings round
all of them.

Richard Ford (11)
Cloudside County
Junior School,
Sandiacre,
Nottingham

The ballad of young Tom Watts

I tell the tale of the surfing scene,
Where Hawaiian waves roll free,
Of young Tom Watts and his life-long dream,
To conquer the foaming sea.

In all his two and twenty years,
His one ambition stayed,
To strive, regardless of his fears,
To ride the perfect wave.

Each morning found him on the beach,
His custom board well waxed,
He knew it was within his reach,
The wave that can't be matched.

He knew what he was looking for,
A tube, a lip, a swell,
A wave to beat the Severn Bore,
The wave his dreams foretell.

He practised in the swirling surf
And learnt to walk the nose,
He carved the waves to bottom turn,
He learnt to hang five toes.

Tom travelled far to Maui Bay,
He found his luck was in,
The surf was up throughout the day,
Just hear the breakers' din!

The waves rose up ten metres high,
Young Tom prepared to go,
He caught a wave, and gave a cry,
As in the pipe he rode.

Alas his joy was quite short-lived,
The wave dumped on the shore,
'Wipe Out', we heard his anguished yell,
Above the ocean's roar.

But Tom was no way beaten yet,
One day, at last he saw,
The seventh wave of a seventh set,
Of a group of seven more.

He *knew* his chance had come at last,
The wave to beat them all,
He launched his board, and paddled fast,
We held our breath enthralled.

The perfect wave approached in time.
Tom sliced hard down the face,
He crouched down low to ride pipe-line,
And felt his body brace.

At last the foaming crest he steered,
Then tragedy befell,
The tube closed down, Tom disappeared,
And left this tale to tell.

But don't feel sad about poor Tom,
Lost in his watery grave,
For you can hear his ghostly song,
'I found my perfect wave!'

Alex Hill (14)
Henry Beaufort School,
Harestock, Winchester,
Hants

Hockey

hit

shouts .... panting _____

.... Avoiding tackles _____

Whistle!!! Sighs of relief _____

$p \to q \quad t \to i \to o \to n \quad g$

$s \to i^{\uparrow} \qquad \qquad i \to n^{\uparrow}$

_____

"TENSION"

Smack — s ≡ w ≡ o ≡ o ≡ p ≡ -dribbling

Hack, cracking sticks,

t l y n u d
h i g m

Sweat

shouts

Hit - THUD

"MISS!"

Cara Leach (13)
Hulme Grammar School for Girls,
Oldham, Lancs

Rock music

Tension is building,
Can you feel it?
You can never be prepared,
No matter how you try.
The guitar howls and screams,
And a drummer fights his kit.
The volume builds up,
And it flows to a crescendo.
You can feel the energy from beneath,
Bursting from the ground, and spiralling up your legs.
It makes you want to run,
It makes you want to shout,
It makes you want to tear down the walls that stop you
    getting out.

Marcus Knight (14)
Wymondham High School,
Wymondham, Norfolk

Record poem

Inside the record label: RECORD POEM BY Sally Clayton 1.12.88 (and the word SCRATCH)

Sally Clayton (12)
The Hayling School,
Hayling Island, Hants

Dancing machine

Growing inspiration
Burning through the smoky mist.
Feel the power surging,
A force you can't resist.

Feel the voltage rising,
When you begin to move.

You're going to shower sparks
When you get into the groove.

You've got to feel the music
Burn up your body heat.
Let the music take control,
You're twisting to the beat.

There's a chain reaction,
And you step into the fire,
You're going to have a good time,
If you turn the music higher.

The floor begins its swaying,
The lights are flashing bright,
There's nobody to stop you now,
You're in the centre light.

There's a burning sensation,
Let the music flow,
Feel the rising madness,
And just let yourself go.

The temperature is cooling,
The lights stop going round,
The music now is fading,
And you're back on level ground.

Sharron Redmond (14)
Litherland High School,
Litherland, Liverpool

The 1990 Cadbury's Poetry Competition

The Cadbury's Books of Children's Poetry contain about 160 selected entries from children of all ages and are illustrated with work from the National Exhibition of Children's Art.

If you would like to enter the 1990 competition whether in the Art, Design or Poetry sections, you can write to this address for an entry form:

Cadbury's National Exhibition of Children's Art
Granby
Altrincham
Cheshire
WA14 5SZ

(Please enclose a stamped/addressed envelope)

Remember – you not only have a chance to feature in the *Cadbury's Eighth Book of Children's Poetry* but also to win a place on the Cadbury Italian Art Tour.

Index of titles

Index of authors